Studies in Canadian Geography

Etudes sur la géographie du Canada

Louis Trot...

917.11   Robinson, John Lewis, 1918-   ed.
Rob   British Columbia; Colombie britannique.
        Ed. by J. Lewis Robinson.   Toronto, University
      of Toronto Press, 1972.
        139 p.   illus., maps.   (Studies in
      Canadian geography)
        Published for the 22nd International
      Geographical Congress, Montreal, 1972.
        Includes bibliography.

RELATED
BOOKS IN   1. British Columbia. I. International
CATALOG   Geographical Congress. 22nd, Montreal, 1972.
UNDER   II. Title: Colombie britannique.
                                        G-8608
                                        G-9445

British Columbia

Colombie britannique

Edited by/Sous la direction de J. Lewis Robinson

published for the 22nd International Geographical Congress
publié à l'occasion du 22e Congrès international de géographie
Montréal 1972

University of Toronto Press

© University of Toronto Press 1972
Toronto and Buffalo

ISBN 0-8020-1922-6 (Cloth)
ISBN 0-8020-6162-1 (Paper)
Microfiche ISBN 0-8020-0259-5

Printed in Canada

Contents

Foreword

The publication of the series, 'Studies in Canadian Geography,' by the organizers of the 22nd International Geographical Congress, introduces to the international community of geographers a new perspective of the regional entities which form this vast country. These studies should contribute to a better understanding, among scholars, students, and the people of Canada, of the geography of their land.

Geographical works embracing the whole of Canada, few in number until recently, have become more numerous during the last few years. This series is original in its purpose of re-evaluating the regional geography of Canada. In the hope of discovering the dynamic trends and the processes responsible for them, the editors and authors of these volumes have sought to interpret the main characteristics and unique attributes of the various regions, rather than follow a strictly inventorial approach.

It is a pleasant duty for me to thank all who have contributed to the preparation of the volume on British Columbia. A special thanks is due to: Mr R.I.K. Davidson of the University of Toronto Press; Mr Geoffrey Lester who guided the Cartography Laboratory of the Department of Geography, University of Alberta in preparing all the illustrations; the Canadian Association of Geographers for its financial support; and the Executive of the Organizing Committee of the 22nd International Geographical Congress. Finally I wish to thank Professor J. Lewis Robinson, Department of Geography, University of British Columbia, for having accepted the editorship of this volume.

LOUIS TROTIER
Chairman
Publications Committee

Avant-propos

Par la publication de cette série d'« Etudes sur la géographie du Canada », les organisateurs du 22e Congrès international de géographie ont voulu profiter de l'occasion qui leur était donnée de présenter à la communauté internationale des géographes une perspective nouvelle des grands ensembles régionaux qui composent cet immense pays. Ils espèrent que ces études contribueront aussi à mieux faire comprendre la géographie de leur pays aux Canadiens eux-mêmes, scientifiques, étudiants ou autres.

Les travaux d'ensemble sur la géographie du Canada, peu nombreux jusqu'à récemment, se sont multipliés au cours des dernières années. L'originalité de cette série provient surtout d'un effort de renouvellement de la géographie régionale du Canada. Les rédacteurs et les auteurs de ces ouvrages ont cherché moins à inventorier leur région qu'à en interpréter les traits majeurs et les plus originaux, dans l'espoir de découvrir les tendances de leur évolution.

C'est pour moi un agréable devoir de remercier et de féliciter tous ceux qui ont contribué d'une manière ou d'une autre à la réalisation de cet ouvrage sur la Colombie britannique. Il convient de mentionner les membres du Comité d'organisation du 22e Congrès international de géographie; M. R.I.K. Davidson, des Presses de l'Université de Toronto; l'Association canadienne des géographes; le département de géographie de l'Université de l'Alberta, à Edmonton, dont le Laboratoire de cartographie a préparé toutes les illustrations de cet ouvrage sous la direction habile et dévouée de M. Geoffrey Lester. Je remercie enfin M. J. Lewis Robinson, professeur de géographie à l'Université de la Colombie britannique, d'avoir accepté d'assumer la direction de cet ouvrage.

LOUIS TROTIER
Président du
Comité des publications

Preface

This volume on British Columbia is one of six regional monographs prepared by the Canadian Association of Geographers for the 1972 meeting of the International Geographical Union in Canada. The purpose of the monograph series is not to present a complete regional or topical study of the selected area, but to provide a flavour of the geographical research that is going on and to point out certain regional characteristics of each part of Canada. Five specific topics which are relevant to the understanding of certain geographical aspects of British Columbia are discussed in this volume. Each of the authors is a faculty member in the Geography Department of the University of British Columbia. The topics follow an introductory chapter by the volume editor describing certain distinctive regional characteristics and evolving areal patterns.

Chapter 2 outlines the history of mainly rural settlement, stopping short of the recent trends in urbanization. The emphasis is on characteristic areal and cultural patterns and formative factors. Chapter 3 deals with two specific elements in the physical environment of the Cordilleran province: its mountains and its rivers and their interrelationships. The hydrological characteristics of river basins in British Columbia are variable in comparison with the rest of Canada, and a detailed knowledge of their behaviour is required for future river management. Chapter 4 describes the general and regional character of British Columbia's economy, and analyses the changing trends in the past decade. The study is done in the context of modern theories of regional economic development, and the spatial structure of the contemporary economy is summarized in a single geographical model. Chapter 5 is concerned with one particular element in the provincial economy – and the most important one – forestry. The areal patterns of the forest resource and changing patterns of utilization are described and interpreted. Chapter 6 describes the evolving patterns of urban settlement around Georgia Strait, in the southwest, where 75 per cent of the provincial population lives. The urban area is dominated by Vancouver, but the city itself is only part of an emerging multicentred metropolitan region.

University of British Columbia
February 1972

J.L.R.

cross sectional map
to density (pop)

Map of BC

1 Areal Patterns and Regional Character

J. LEWIS ROBINSON

British Columbia is a mountainous province. Great contrasts within small areas are characteristic of the natural environment, and there are also wide contrasts in population densities within the province. It is a region of urban people, with agriculture entirely lacking over large areas or confined to certain narrow valleys or floodplains. This urban population is concentrated in one small area, the southwestern corner of the province, where 75 per cent of the people live. In the middle of the nineteenth century, cut off by the mountain barrier and the empty Interior Plains from the other colonies in eastern Canada, and far from 'Mother England' by sea around Cape Horn, the western province experienced isolation; and even today its people often exhibit varying attitudes of independence.

The physical environment of British Columbia has its distinct regional characteristics, which differ from those of other parts of Canada. Some comparable spectacular landforms are found in mountainous Baffin and Ellesmere islands in the northeastern Arctic, but their extent is not as great as the 600 miles of peaks, ridges, and valleys across southern British Columbia. Although these mountains seem to be a jumbled mass of peaks locally, and stretch endlessly to the horizon when viewed from the air, they have quite specific areal patterns and are subdivided into smaller subregional units (see Figure 3.3). For example, despite numerous maps published outside of Canada which spread the name 'Rocky Mountains' across much of British Columbia and even into the Yukon and Alaska, the Rockies are a specific line of local mountain ranges extending north-westward from Montana along the Alberta–British Columbia border, and terminating at the broad plain of the Liard River in northeastern British Columbia (see Figure 1.1). The western landform boundary of the Rocky Mountains is the Rocky Mountain Trench, one of the longest, continuous valleys on the earth's surface, extending from Flathead Lake, Montana, to the Liard Plain on the northern boundary of British Columbia. Other mountain systems to the westward, such as the Columbia and Cassiar-Omineca mountains, are separate landform regions. They have similar

1.1
Relief Model of British Columbia in Provincial Museum, Victoria

internal characteristics of high, sharp peaks, narrow U-shaped valleys, and steep slopes (see Chapter 3 for details).

In contrast, the landform regions of the Interior and Stikine plateaus are undulating interior basins with generally level horizons; locally, however, they are deeply cut by rivers and canyons. The river valleys of the interior usually have narrow strips and terraces of level land above the slightly entrenched rivers. The only large delta and floodplain in the province is that of the Fraser River in the southwest, and this area of level land has the highest density of population in the province.

Contrasts in climate are characteristic of mountainous regions, and British Columbia is no exception. Because most of the weather stations are in the valley bottoms, where the settlements are, these contrasts often have to be inferred from vegetation differences or other indirect environmental information. The greatest amounts of precipitation recorded in Canada – more than 150 inches annually – are among the distinctive features of some of the west-facing slopes of the Insular and Coast mountains. And only 200 to 300 miles away, in the southern interior valleys, some of the driest stations outside of the Arctic report less than 10 inches of annual precipitation. Most of the coastal precipitation falls on the lowland settlements as rain during the winter months, and blankets the higher elevations of the nearby mountains with snow. Although long-time residents of Vancouver are wont to boast that it 'seldom snows here,' a cold air mass from the Interior Plateau can spill westward along the Fraser Valley, chilling the usual mild, moist Pacific air masses and resulting in the dumping of tons of snow on the coastal cities for a few days at a time.

Another regional characteristic is the mild winter climate of coastal British Columbia, the warmest in Canada with January averages of 30° to 35° F. But inland the linear valleys are open to the southward penetration of cold air masses from Alaska and the Yukon, and settlements in these valleys record many days of below zero winter temperatures. Indeed, winter temperatures in the interior of the Cordillera differ little from those experienced across the Interior Plains. In summer the southwest coast is normally cool (about 60° F average in July) and sunny for many weeks, when high-pressure ridges form over it and deflect storms northward. This climatic characteristic is another element which is unique in southern Canada. But a few hundred miles away residents and visitors in the southern valleys can experience some of the hottest temperatures recorded in Canada. The coastal climate is therefore different from that of the rest of Canada, whereas the remainder of British Columbia has some climates which are similar to those east of the mountains.

The vertical contrasts in climate are apparent in the horizontal zonation of vegetation on the mountain slopes. The mild and wet coastal climate has nourished the largest trees known in Canada. However, temperatures decrease with altitude and steep, rocky slopes have little soil; therefore tree size and density decrease at about 5000 feet, and generally the alpine slopes above 6000 feet are treeless. In northern British Columbia the upper tree line may be about 3500 feet above sea level, leaving only narrow strips of forest cover along the river valleys. Although the presence of grassland is obvious to travellers through the dry valleys of southern British Columbia, it occupies only narrow strips or small basins and the total area is not large. Cattle ranching in the interior therefore operates more in a parkland vegetation environment than does ranching on southern Alberta's grassland.

The variety in the natural environment of British Columbia offered a wide choice of natural resources for Europeans who entered the region in increasing numbers near the close of the nineteenth century. Except for the large cities in southwestern British Columbia, settlements are based mainly on the exploitation of one particular natural resource. This resource-based economy of British Columbia is similar to that of many settlements in the Canadian Shield and the Atlantic Provinces in eastern Canada. The resource developments in the province have evolved in rather specific areal patterns.

Forestry is the main segment of British Columbia's economy (see Chapter 5). Utilization of the large trees started in the southwestern corner of the province and the wood-processing industry is still concentrated there. The forests on the coastal lowlands near Vancouver, Nanaimo, and Victoria were cut first in local small mills and processed for export. As forests farther away along the coast were cut, a log-transporting technology developed to carry the logs to the large mills in or near the cities around the Strait of Georgia. Improvements in transport technology – from the Davis rafts of the 1930s to modern self-dumping log barges – permitted the exploitation of a longer coastal hinterland to supply the urban sawmills. The mills and settlements around the Strait of Georgia, and northward along the Inside Passage, became an integrated, functional region linked together by movements and services related to the forest industry.

Prior to 1940, because wood products were mainly for export by water to northwestern Europe or the eastern United States, the forest industry concentrated on the coast, and mainly near the ports in the south. After 1950, increased world demand, plus improved rail and road transport into the untapped forest reserves of the interior, permitted an areal expansion of the industry into the interior. Nodes of intense utilization arose at transport junctions such as Prince George and Kamloops, and in southeastern British Columbia, which was closest to the market in the north-central United States. The forest industry of the interior is now establishing geographical patterns of concentration, and corporate integration of processing, similar to that which developed on the coast prior to 1940.

The geography of the west coast fishery is different from that of the Atlantic coast. The five main species of Pacific salmon constitute most of the west coast fish catch, and the industry has adapted to the natural habits and migrations of these fish. Salmon enter the river mouths in late summer heading for spawning waters in the interior lakes and shallow headwater tributaries, and fishermen assemble off these river mouths to catch the salmon en route. Fish canneries were established at or near the mouths of most rivers along the coast late in the nineteenth century, but the greatest concentration was near the Fraser and Skeena rivers which had the largest drainage basins and therefore usually had the most fish production. Gradually fishing technology improved so that larger and faster fishing vessels, with better gear and larger carrying capacity, could harvest a larger area away from the river mouths. Thus the need decreased for many small canneries dispersed along the coast, and the processing industry concentrated in large canneries at a few central places. By the 1960s the former linear pattern of salmon canneries had become one of concentration at only the mouths of the Skeena and Fraser rivers, where there were shipping connections for export. This process of spatial concentration, arising from corporate integration and new fishing technology, is now complete on the west coast; in contrast, the process is just beginning on the east coast of Canada.

Through more than a century of British Columbia mining history the geographical patterns of development have illustrated some consistent areal trends. From 1890 to 1905 the Kootenay region of the southeast was one of the most important mining areas of Canada while the rest of the province was struggling to create a viable economy. The southeast is well mineralized, and as a mining region it functions around the large smelter-refinery at Trail, where a variety of ores from the region are taken for processing. For more than 80 years mining has been a major impetus in the economy of the Kootenays; abandoned mines, slag piles, and decaying houses – as well as modern efficient mines and new planned towns – are significant elements in the regional landscape.

Because minerals are produced for export outside of the region, those mineralized areas of the Coast and Insular mountains accessible to ocean transport continue to support producing mines. As in other mining regions, individual mines close and new ones open but the coastal area as a whole remains a producer. In the early 1970s the capital and markets of

Japan provided the stimuli for opening new copper and iron mines there. The younger sediments of northeastern British Columbia have a different geological history and a different type of mineralization. From there petroleum and natural gas are transported by pipeline to markets in urban southwestern British Columbia and the adjoining United States. New mines have also been opened in several places in the Interior Plateau, giving a more dispersed pattern to mining activity than in preceding decades. As noted earlier, this dispersal of mining and associated towns is characteristic of the resource-based, single-function activity of the economy in the interior of the province.

The availability of hydroelectric power has aided resource development in British Columbia just as it has in the Canadian Shield of eastern Canada. British Columbia has the fortunate natural endowment of heavy precipitation, sloping landforms, many lakes for water storage, and numerous rivers. Together, these environmental conditions are excellent for the production of hydropower. To these natural elements man has added dams, turbines, and transmission lines to the urban and industrial markets.

Waterpower development has shown one pattern of clustered concentration and another of dispersal. Throughout the history of settlement in British Columbia the largest cities, major rural population, and most industries have clustered in the southwest corner of the province. Power for this market was supplied from small sites in the Coast Mountains near Vancouver or on short rivers on southern Vancouver Island. As transmission technology improved power could be produced at more distant sites, such as Bridge River east of the Coast Mountains. Thus, a cluster of relatively small power plants evolved in southwestern British Columbia near the urban and industrial markets. Elsewhere, power developments were dispersed and supplied only local needs. For example, power for the large Trail smelter-refinery and for cities of the southeast came mainly from several plants on the Kootenay River. In the northwest, the Nechako River was dammed in the early 1950s and diverted back through a tunnel beneath the Coast Mountains to produce power at Kemano for the large aluminium smelter at Kitimat. In the late 1960s power was developed in the fourth corner of the province, on the Peace River of the northeast, partially as a result of improvements in long-distance transmission technology. In the 1970s the two areal patterns of concentration in the southwest and dispersal in the three other corners of the province will become part of one large provincial network. Because there are no large underdeveloped waterpower sites near the growing industrial and urban markets of the southwest, future power will have to be supplied from local thermal or nuclear plants as well as being transported from Mica Dam on the

Columbia River and from increased capacity of the Bennett Dam on the Peace River. The undeveloped central part of British Columbia, the Fraser River and its tributaries, remains as a region of large potential waterpower where priority for water use is at present given to the production of salmon.

The preceding remarks have noted the areal patterns of resource development in forestry, mining, and waterpower. No comments have been made in the recreational use of the spectacular and varied environments of British Columbia. This use of the natural environment may yet prove to be one of the most valuable 'natural resources' of the province. As in the Canadian Shield of eastern Canada, the 'empty' areas of British Columbia will have increasing value as population densities increase in the rest of the continent. As in the rugged Shield also, agriculture is a relatively minor activity in British Columbia. Only about 5 per cent of the provincial population is engaged in agriculture. Climate and soils in most valleys are favourable for agriculture, and urban markets are nearby, but the amount of suitable level land in the valleys is small. Agricultural settlement was significant, however, in the early occupation of certain sections of the province and these events are described in Chapter 2.

Much of the resource-based activity throughout the province is focused directly or indirectly in Metropolitan Vancouver. The head offices of the resource-converting companies are in Vancouver; most of the interior products funnel to the ports around the Strait of Georgia for export. Half of the population of British Columbia lives in Greater Vancouver and another 25 per cent lives nearby in the Lower Fraser Valley and in or near Victoria on southern Vancouver Island. In many ways Vancouver has the same internal urban landscapes as cities of eastern Canada: highrise office buildings and apartments, rows of ranch-style homes, suburban shopping centres, and low sprawling factories and warehouses along the outer highways. In other ways the urban patterns within the metropolitan region are distinct, and the urban system arising around the Strait of Georgia region is an example of a functioning multicentred urban region. These characteristics are discussed in Chapter 6.

The other cities of British Columbia, outside of the urban core in the southwest, are centres of their surrounding regions. In the valley-oriented, dispersed areas of settlement in the interior the resource-based activities are focused upon one main and growing city. The linkages between these cities and with Vancouver have been strengthened in the past two decades (see Chapter 6). In internal form and function many of these interior cities are similar to the service towns and resource-based settlements east of the mountains in the rest of Canada.

Mountainous British Columbia has distinctive variety within small areas in climate, vegetation, soils, land use, and settlement. It has a heartland in the southwest which is functionally connected with a coastal and interior hinterland. The region is one where the emphasis is on the development of natural resources, and as such has many characteristics of its economy similar to the Canadian Shield region and, to a lesser extent, the Atlantic Provinces. The urban development of the southwestern Cordillera is like that of metropolitan Montreal and Toronto, but British Columbia lacks the wider network of interconnected large cities that is one of the regional characteristics of the Great Lakes–St Lawrence Lowland. Within British Columbia the two main subregions are the coast, with its distinctive climate and urban concentration, and the growing resource-oriented settlements of the interior. These regional subdivisions have been fundamental in the past history of areal occupation of the province, but improved transport in the past two decades is breaking down the division and a new set of areal patterns is evolving on a provincial scale.

2 Settlement

ALFRED H. SIEMENS

The visitor to British Columbia is likely to find its cultural landscapes rather new and hurriedly put together. The log houses and barns of initial settlers can still be seen from the north-central region and the Peace River country through to the Kootenays. There are mixed echoes here and there of European and other homelands; one sees the debris of false beginnings but also many new and viable solutions everywhere to the old problems of livelihood, shelter, circulation, and leisure. The recent changes are indicated in various ways. In places, unused and deteriorating farm buildings litter the landscape, reflecting the demise of the small farm of 25 and more years ago but also indicating a healthy improvement in agricultural technology and a pragmatic change in the interests of many rural residents. Cattle ranches have become guest ranches, orchards have been made into campgrounds, and marginally productive agricultural land cut up into high-priced summer-home lots. The corollary is seen in all the modern trappings of 'agro-businesses.' Community halls that once served as social centres for their respective communities have generally fallen into disuse in favour of facilities in the larger towns. The general store at the crossroads has atrophied and shopping centres have increased in number. The growth of any town at all well connected is clearly visible along the profile of any through-street.

The purpose of this chapter is to portray the essentials of British Columbian settlement patterns and to sketch the process of their development. The emphasis will be on rural landscapes; the urban scene is discussed in Chapter 6. 'Settlement' in this context means mainly non-Indian settlement, a variant on a generally familiar North American theme. Some pre-contact antecedents will be noted, together with various aspects of the impact on Indian lifeways.

Of particular concern are the effects from place to place of a series of specific formative factors: remoteness, mountainous topography, establishment of the border, the exploitation of gold and other non-agricultural

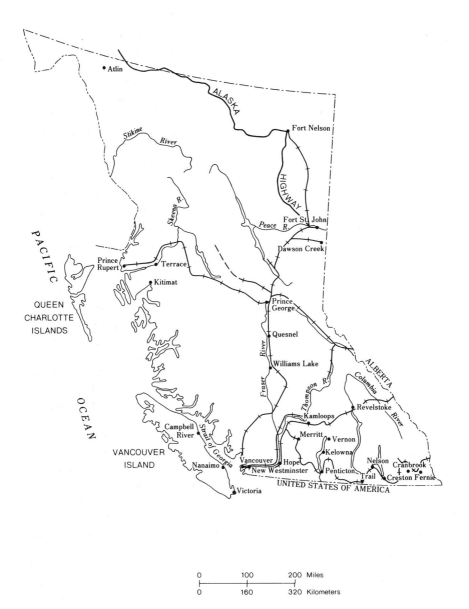

2.1
Main Cities and Railways of British Columbia

resources, institutional constraints, environmental attractions, mixed cultural heritage, technological change, urbanization. Fundamental to all of them, but outside of the scope of this discussion, are broader influences on the occupance of the Americas, such as economic problems in Europe and other source areas, as well as elusive factors like the opportunity to cut tiresome old ties and begin again on a frontier. Some of the more specific factors were effective for only a short time; others have remained so until the present day. Some were more noticeable in one area than another. Up to the time of the Gold Rush, one can deal with them in eras applicable to the entire province. After that the development of the individual regions varies considerably, and although some parallelism is noticeable, different patterns and problems emerge in each.

The late start and the tardiness of the early phases of the settlement of British Columbia are attributable in large part to its remoteness from Europe, especially before the cutting of the Panama Canal, as well as from the developing colonies along the St Lawrence River and the eastern seaboard. Settlers were not easily attracted, particularly since land offers were more liberal to the south, and colonial affairs could hardly be administered with dispatch. Surface travel and settlement in British Columbia have been from the beginning, and still are to a large extent, forced through the weir of the province's linear landforms; these go far to account for attenuated patterns of cultural features, as well as the general similarity between early settlement patterns and those of today.

The international border, drawn across the grain of the landforms in 1846, impeded movement along the well-established north-south routes and encouraged an entry from the west. The desire to maintain British sovereignty north of this line made it urgently necessary to provide east-west British Columbian transportation routes, to hurry agricultural settlement by British subjects immediately north of the border, and to enhance in every possible way the political control of the colony over its land.

The most important single impetus for early rural and urban settlement in the province was the discovery of gold along the Fraser River. Fur-bearing animals and salmon had attracted some concentrated settlement before this; other minerals and marketable stands of timber exerted their attractions later. The exploitation of each of these non-agricultural resources gave rise to characteristic communities, as well as supporting farms, mills, and other facilities within range of economical transport. The exhaustion of some resources, notably mineral ore bodies, time and again removed the economic base from various communities leaving a clutter of abandoned buildings. Changing technology and improved transportation have in recent decades diminished the need for settlement concentration at isolated logging, fishing, and related industrial sites.

Pre-emption was the means of obtaining agricultural land during the Gold Rush. This allowed virtually free initial occupance of unsurveyed land by any British subject with payment required if and when the survey could be carried out. After 1873 the grid pattern of surveying, already in use in some areas of British Columbia since the early 1860s, was applied with better measurement control and greater administrational firmness, whether suitable to the terrain or not. At about this time pre-emption was belatedly replaced by homesteading, which allowed a man 160 acres or more for a nominal payment and the promise to live on and improve the land. With the coming of the railways, the provincial government and the railway companies promoted settlement. Unfortunately, overoptimistic or misleading advertisements brought many settlers to land that turned out to be unsuitable for agriculture. Free land grants are available now in only the remotest regions, where land is suitable for recreational use at best; the exception is in the Peace River region where agricultural home-steads are still possible. There is, of course, a lively real estate market. New farms are now usually developed by amalgamation and improve-ment of existing farms. Effective planning for, and restrictions on, the development of rural and urban settlement are relatively recent for most parts of the province.

The availability of land for agriculture in climatically moderate and often strikingly beautiful settings became an important attraction once the swarming of the gold miners had subsided and people wrote letters home, or published regional descriptions. In this century, many prairie farmers, tired of droughts and harsh winters, have moved to British Columbia per-manently or for the winters. Climate and setting also provided the basic prerequisites for settlement related to tourism, recreational land use, and retirement.

The settlers of varied but predominantly British background that re-sponded to the attractions of British Columbia could have been expected to modify their new surroundings in terms of those in which they had their roots. However, by the time they had reached British Columbia, many of them were several times removed from their cultural source areas, having come west in stages and over several generations, and having absorbed a good deal along the way. Furthermore, in any one community there was often considerable turnover in the population within short periods of time. Attempting to decipher the origin and significance of features now seen in landscape as indicators of cultural background is therefore often difficult, if not pointless. Nevertheless, here and there within the rural and urban landscapes certain peculiar elements, either relict or currently functional, may still be attributed to the cultural heritage of certain groups, whether racially, ethnically, or religiously defined.

Change in the means of transportation, one aspect of broader technological change, strongly influenced the direction and over-all pattern of settlement. Certain waterways and connective trails blazed in earlier times allowed the first entries. The wagon roads facilitated the movement of miners and settlers into the interior and provided the orientation for most subsequent settlement. The building of railways across the width of the province revolutionized economies in region after region, allowed surges of in-migration, and gave rise to numerous service settlements along their routes. The recent vast improvement in the highway network has facilitated the orientation of the entire province toward the cities of its southwest corner.

The current process of urbanization emanating from the cities of the province, particularly Vancouver, has brought the most pervasive changes in settlement patterns. The use of land on the peripheries of cities has changed drastically as they have extended their political boundaries. The high degree of mobility, the economic concentration, and the sophistication of mass communications characterizing life in the modern city have had their effects on the remotest farms and corner hamlets.

FIRST ENTRIES BY EUROPEANS

The coast of British Columbia remained one of the least-known areas of the world well into the eighteenth century. The Spaniards reached it in 1774 and came again in 1790 to establish a small settlement on the west coast of Vancouver Island. It was a base for some limited fur trading and an attempt at military control, but lasted only until 1795. The first more substantial economic interest in the coastline dates from Captain Cook's voyage of 1778 and the subsequent development of the sea-otter fur trade with the Orient. Permanent coastal settlement did not come until 1843, with the establishment of Fort Victoria. It was a key fort in the Hudson's Bay Company system, a replacement for Fort Vancouver on the Columbia River. Its establishment represented a response to the northwestward push of American settlement.

Another entry was achieved overland from the northeast in 1793 by Alexander Mackenzie. A number of fur trading forts were established in the early years of the nineteenth century throughout what was called New Caledonia, a vast fur trading district in north-central British Columbia centred on Fort St James.

The fur trading posts varied considerably in structure and equipment. Some were substantial settlements with elaborate facilities within the palisades and agricultural lands beyond. However, only company employees lived at the posts. The cultivation around the forts, for the subsistence of those living within, as well as for a limited trade, constituted the beginnings of agriculture in the province. Colonization of surrounding land through immigration was discouraged by the Hudson's Bay Company, the repository of British authority in British Columbia until the middle of the nineteenth century. Nevertheless, the forts and their connecting routes may be seen as the first sketch of the future settlement pattern; as well as the first indication of the influence of landforms. Some of the information about the terrain gained by those who travelled along the fur brigade routes was eventually used by settlers.

Early contact with the white man during the fur trading period stimulated Indian cultures, particularly those of the coastal tribes, to new growth (Duff 1965, pp. 53–4). The new wealth, materials, tools, and ideas brought in proved a potent stimulus to arts, crafts, trade, technology, social and ceremonial life. The disruptive influences that eventually set in included diseases, alcohol, the encroachment of white settlers on traditional Indian lands, the imposition of outside laws, the suppression of native customs, and the persuasion of missionaries who advocated new ways of life. An aboriginal population that may have numbered at least 80,000 before white contact had been reduced to 70,000 people by 1835, the year of the first count.

THE RUSH FOR GOLD (1858–66)

When the news of the discovery of gold along the Fraser River reached San Francisco in February 1858, an exodus from Californian diggings began. About 25,000 to 30,000 men, mainly Americans, arrived along the lower Fraser in the spring and summer of 1858. Most were initially interested only in gold, but many pre-empted land after unsuccessful stints along the gold-bearing streams. Those who shrewdly decided to sell food to the miners instead of going to the diggings themselves quickly took up advantageous farming locations. This was a small affair, as gold rushes of the nineteenth century went, but it had a significant impact in British Columbia.

In 1860 interest shifted from the diggings along the Fraser to the creeks of the Cariboo country, where the most sustained and lucrative phase of British Columbia's Gold Rush took place. Between 1860 and 1866 there were further rushes to the Stikine and Peace rivers, as well as into the southern Kootenays and the 'Big Bend' section of the Columbia River.

In each region that it affected the gold mining activity eventually left pitted creek beds, denuded hillsides, and ghost towns, but also permanently altered the pattern of settlement, and spurred the development of agriculture, commerce, and to some extent industry. The province's first towns, New Westminster, Victoria, and Yale, grew up as the main supply centres for the gold miners. The foot and pack trails which had served the fur traders were displaced by wagon roads. These necessitated different routes to allow for gentler grades and wider road beds. Road houses, ranches, and grist mills were established along them to provision travellers. Farming was stimulated beyond these main routes as well, notably in the Okanagan Valley, where several sizable ranches were established.

The gold era resulted in a further and catastrophic decrease in the Indian population, mainly as a result of a smallpox epidemic. Of the approximately 60,000 Indians estimated to be in British Columbia in 1858, about 30,000 remained in 1866 (Duff 1965, p. 44). There was also the inevitable further encroachment on Indian land. Governor Douglas set out to conclude treaties with the Indians, extinguishing their title by purchase with funds of the Hudson's Bay Company, to whom the colonization of Vancouver Island had been entrusted. He also set aside numerous reserves at the locations and in the sizes the Indians favoured. Douglas' successors were not able to conclude further treaties, and moreover were much less generous in setting aside reserves. The issue of Indian lands is still unresolved. Indian spokesmen insist that an extinction of title by payment or a return of the land must be negotiated.

AFTER THE GOLD RUSH

Vancouver Island
In the settlement of Vancouver Island and the smaller islands nearby the influence of the whole range of factors outlined above has been felt. Substantive settlement began with the discovery of gold, but some antecedents are pertinent.

In taking on the responsibility for settling the colony of Vancouver Island, the Hudson's Bay Company obligated itself to bring in a stable British farming population in return for 10 per cent of the proceeds from sales of land, licences, and royalties, which were themselves to go into roads and other improvements. It was ironic, of course, that a fur trading company, traditionally opposed to settlement surrounding its posts, should be granted this responsibility. In fact, little colonization was achieved because of the price of the land and other restrictions.

Victoria reaped the benefits of Douglas's instructions that all persons going to the mainland gold mines must first obtain a licence in Victoria and then travel by ship under Hudson's Bay Company charter from Victoria to the Fraser River. The arrival of gold seekers, some of them willing to invest their money in Victoria even before reaching the mines, sustained a land boom while their licence fees provided public capital. It was hoped that this rapidly growing town would come to rival San Francisco, but this was not to be. It had the disadvantage of being separated from the mainland by the Strait of Georgia. Its hinterland was considerably smaller than that of San Francisco, and was shared with New Westminster. Furthermore, San Francisco was already established as a manufacturing centre for the entire coast, allowing Victoria only a distributional function.

The environmental attractions, the liberalized terms for settlement that obtained with the termination of Hudson's Bay Company control, and the initiation of a system of pre-emption, plus the common expectation that much of the wealth generated by gold would eventually find its way to the island, generated a considerable demand for agricultural land on southeastern Vancouver Island and the nearby larger Gulf Islands. By the early 1860s, substantial settlement had begun in the Cowichan and Comox valleys, at the head of Alberni Inlet, and on Gabriola Island. In most cases agriculture in the most favourable locations came first, followed by logging in the surrounding areas, particularly after the construction of roads and railways. Nanaimo, established in 1852 by the Hudson's Bay Company to protect and serve its coal mines, had grown into a considerable settlement by the beginning of the next decade.

In 1884 a wagon road was completed between Victoria and Nanaimo; in 1886 the Esquimalt and Nanaimo railway was also ready. The road served agricultural pockets; the railway allowed extensive logging and fostered related industries. Both helped to bring in more and more people along their routes.

On Vancouver Island, as elsewhere in British Columbia, the railroad era brought a great increase in immigration and raised agricultural as well as urban land values. Most of the people who came to Vancouver Island in this period were British; they reinforced the British element already established there by retired Hudson's Bay Company officers and Royal Navy men. Many were younger sons with private incomes, or 'remittance men' as they came to be called. They relied on their farms for a good deal of their livelihood, but evidently were not as driving or ambitious as the many settlers elsewhere on the continent who began with virtually nothing (Ormsby 1945, p. 15).

Vancouver Island and the Gulf Islands received a good deal of the Canadian migration westward, as well as soldier settlement, before and after World War II. Some in-migrants still settled on farms, but more and more came to work in the forests or the lumber-mills, which by the 1930s had become economically pre-eminent (see Chapter 5). After 1945, the number of retirement or summer homes on seaside lots increased until land values there approached those in urban residential areas. Many scenically located old farms were able to render a satisfying monetary return at last when they were subdivided and sold.

Lower Fraser Valley
In the settlement of the Lower Fraser Valley, or the Lower Mainland, as the region is sometimes called, all the formative factors were operative, as they were on Vancouver Island, but with different results. The variety and impact of ethnic and racial elements is more noticeable in the Lower Fraser Valley than in the other regions. It is the home of more than half of the population of the province (Table 2.1). The current processes of urbanization and socioeconomic integration are most strongly felt there as well. There are gloomy forecasts of a super city from tidewater to Hope.

Unsurveyed land was opened for pre-emption in the Lower Fraser Valley in 1860. Most early holdings were river-oriented, linked by 'landings' to the steamship traffic along the river, and all were eventually connected by trails to the old Yale Road, which provided east-west land transportation on the south side of the Fraser River.

Much of this early settlement took place on the lowlands, which were subject to flooding. The flood threat was outweighed by the advantages of accessibility and the light cover of deciduous trees or grasses. Some settlers ventured into the heavily wooded glacial uplands, such as those south of the river and west of Abbotsford, but these upland areas were not extensively settled until they had been logged over around the time of World War I. The many discarded logs and the massive stumps made the logged areas very difficult to clear, especially before the widespread use of dynamite and the later introduction of the bulldozer in the 1940s. Remnants of the early forest, as well as the stumps and logging debris, are still to be seen in the least developed corners of the Lower Mainland.

The flood of 1894, which caused much property damage and some loss of life, pointed up the inadequacy of the few existing private dikes and the

Table 2.1   Ethnic and racial groups in British Columbia and Census Division 4 (essentially the Lower Fraser Valley), 1961*

	B.C.	Census Div. 4	No. 4 as a percentage of B.C.
Total	1,629,082	907,531	55.7
British Isles	966,881	551,320	57.0
Other European			
French	66,970	34,686	51.7
German	118,926	65,450	55.0
Scandinavian	96,792	52,501	54.2
Netherlands	60,176	37,533	62.3
Ukrainian	35,640	20,722	58.1
Italian	38,399	19,523	50.8
Polish	24,870	14,648	58.8
Russian	27,448	10,944	39.8
Austrian	18,084	10,857	60.0
Hungarian	12,833	7,395	57.6
Finnish	10,037	5,786	57.6
Jewish	5,113	4,837	94.6
Czech and Slovak	8,482	4,232	49.8
Other	30,942	17,942	57.9
Asiatic			
Chinese	24,227	17,542	72.4
Japanese	10,424	6,072	58.2
Other Oriental	5,648	2,923	51.7
Negro	1,012	836	82.6
Not stated	27,364	16,523	60.3

*From Dominion Bureau of Statistics, *1961 Census of Canada*, Bull. 1.2–5, Ref. Table 37, pp. 25–6.

urgent need for a substantial integrated system. Within a decade, a system of dikes had been completed, protecting most of the regions subject to flooding. The scene was set for an expansion of settlement and the development of a sizable dairying industry in the lowlands.

Official action was taken as early as 1878 to drain Sumas Lake, the great impediment to east-west transportation through the Lower Mainland south of the Fraser River. It was not until 1920, however, that construction work was actually begun. Four years later the last water had been pumped out of the lake, and agricultural work could begin on the 9000 acres of choice land newly exposed. New cropping patterns could be established on the 2000 acres of peripheral lands formerly flooded every year, but now secured. Before drainage, farm buildings in the peripheral areas had to be set on ridges; now they could be located anywhere.

The economy of the province was profoundly affected and its pattern of trading realigned by the completion of the Canadian Pacific Railway through the Lower Fraser Valley in 1885. This brought in new settlers but did not greatly change the settlement pattern. The proximity to the river of the Canadian Pacific and the subsequently completed Canadian National tended to reinforce the already existent riverine concentration of settlement, particularly along the north shore.

The construction of the British Columbia Electric Railway south of the Fraser River had a more marked effect on the settlement pattern. Its various early lines out of Vancouver promoted suburbanization. The completion of a bridge across the Fraser River at New Westminster in 1904, and the rail line to Chilliwack in 1910, gave farmers south of the river access to the New Westminster and Vancouver markets. It encouraged new agricultural settlement at a number of points and gave rise to new service centres, some of which prospered and others of which are now only names on old maps. The situation of Chilliwack, the eastern terminus of the BCER, was greatly enhanced; Cloverdale and Abbotsford became transportation foci. Electric power could be diverted from the railway's transmission lines for lumbering and sawmilling. The friendly 'milk-run' trains, with their characteristic whistle, were soon surrounded with folklore. All this was relegated to the past by the phasing out of passenger service in the late 1940s and the shift to diesel fuel in the early 1950s.

The improvement of roads in the Lower Fraser Valley and the shifts in their routes are basic to recent changes in the settlement pattern. As roads were rerouted, commerce adjusted itself, new centres sprang up, and older ones were eclipsed. Soon unsightly ribbon developments stretched along the main highways out of the metropolitan area. The two main mid-twentieth-century arteries, the old Trans-Canada Highway, south of the river, and the Lougheed Highway, north of the river, have been overshadowed by the new freeway.

From 1901 to 1911 the provincial population rose from 179,000 to 394,000, a generous doubling. Of this increase, 44 per cent was concentrated in Vancouver and a further 15 per cent spread over the remainder of the Lower Mainland. Although the Fraser Valley's share of the provincial increase declined in the following decades, the expansion of urban and rural population in the valley continued briskly. This in-migration further diversified an already varied ethnic and racial composition in the Fraser Valley.

Among those who responded to the attractions of the Lower Mainland, the British element of the population was first and has remained numerically dominant. They affected the form of the cultural landscape profoundly, but it is difficult to decipher precisely the 'Britishness' in it, mixed as it is with elements the British settlers adopted along their way westward through North America. It has so far proved more feasible to analyse the impact on the landscape and the involvement in settlement process of some of the valley's more distinctive, smaller groups. The Chinese, for example, came as indentured labourers for the construction of the Canadian Pacific Railway, and soon they and the native Indians provided inexpensive labour in the salmon canneries on the channels of the Fraser River mouth. They are now mainly urban people. In the settlements of the interior the Chinese own many of the cafes, and in the older residential districts of Vancouver they operate many corner grocery stores. Their impact is clearest in Vancouver's Chinatown, which originated as a ghetto-like refuge for single Cantonese returning from the gold fields and also those later left unemployed by the completion of the Canadian Pacific Railway.

Japanese men seeking employment began arriving in the 1880s and soon were noticeable in lumber-milling, railroad construction, shipping, and fish-canning. Steveston, on the mouth of the south arm of the Fraser, was a Japanese town by 1926. As wives and families arrived, many Japanese went into small fruit and vegetable farming elsewhere in the Lower Fraser Valley. The anti-Oriental feeling that flared frequently in British Columbia for many years climaxed for the Japanese in 1942 in their evacuation eastward. The boats, stores, and farms left behind went for bargain prices to remaining residents or new settlers, including demobilized soldiers.

Sikhs began arriving around the turn of the century and soon became preferred manpower in the sawmills, around which they settled in clusters. Eventually they also took up agriculture and trucking. Their temples, saris, beards, and turbans added a touch of the exotic to the Fraser Valley picture. These outwardly distinctive features have now faded, as have those of other groups in the valley.

Another cultural element was introduced into the Lower Mainland by the French-Canadians who were recruited in Quebec lumber-camps in 1909 for work in the lumber-mills, particularly the Fraser Mills east of New Westminster. In part, they were meant to replace Oriental labourers. They began the community of Maillardville, in which they established various distinctive institutions.

In 1928 the Mennonites, a people of mixed German and Dutch origin, but of distinctive religious persuasion, established Yarrow, the one settlement in the Lower Fraser Valley that approaches an agricultural village in form. Yarrow is a backwater now. Clearbrook, just west of Abbotsford, is the main Mennonite community, a residential and retirement centre with its own particular set of institutions. German is still in everyday use among the older people there, but in occupational and other respects there is little to distinguish the Mennonites from the surrounding population.

Among the most recent in-migrants have been the Dutch, more than half of whom live in the metropolitan area. The rural Dutch have helped materially to revitalize the dairy industry by buying out farmers who were without successors, funds, or the will to continue farming. In the 1950s and 1960s this was a good way for young immigrant couples, as most of the Dutch settlers were, to begin on their own. They are widely seen as shrewd and hard-working innovators, but it is difficult to say how much age and time of entry rather than 'Dutchness' have had to do with their success (Siemens 1968, pp. 117–38).

Pitt Polder, the Lower Fraser Valley name most often associated with the Dutch, took on that character almost by accident. A low area south of Pitt Lake was purchased in 1950 by the Dutch-owned Pitt Polder Company and subsequently drained. Its first three tenants were Dutchmen who had helped to build the dikes. The company was ready to welcome non-Dutch settlers, but the first families attracted others of the same background. The ordered and almost antiseptic landscape created in the Polder contrasts markedly with adjoining Pitt Meadows, which was settled in the early years of the colony's history by people of varied background and is now a jumble of farms, 'hobby farms,' residential subdivisions, and ribbon commercial developments.

The Lower Fraser Valley also has its unimposing Indian enclaves, still located according to the old logic near former fishing and hunting sites. Inadequate conditions on the reserves are by now widely known and decried. The residences are almost uniformly substandard, and the reserve lands are little used by the Indians themselves. However, most bands have leased parts of their reserves for agriculture, lumbering, industry, commerce, or residential development. This brings an assured annual income, but is probably not as profitable as direct involvement in production or real estate development.

The Middle Fraser Region

The Gold Rush had its most romantic and lucrative phases here and also its most striking impact on the cultural landscape. The interest of the miners shifted upstream from the lower Fraser in 1860 to the vicinity of the present towns of Lytton and Lillooet, and then northeast to the gold-bearing creek beds of the 'Cariboo,' where Barkerville and a few lesser ghost towns are still to be seen.

First entry was by trail from the north end of Harrison Lake to Lillooet. Soon the principal route to the gold diggings was the famous Cariboo Road, constructed between 1860 and 1865. It connected Yale, Lytton, and Clinton to Alexandria on the Fraser River, from where steamboats plied northward to Quesnel.

Ranches and road houses were established at convenient intervals like beads on a string, to serve transients and their animals. They provided cattle, hay, vegetables, grain, and in places rudimentary milling facilities as well. Some of the early 'mile houses' survived to become the nuclei for present service centres. With the lapse of the Gold Rush, many ranches lost their market and were sold or abandoned. At the same time much farm property was consolidated into the hands of a fortunate few. Eventually, the strong orientation of farm settlement towards the main roads diminished and ranches began to locate closer to water and choice grazing lands.

The construction of railways, from the completion of the Canadian Pacific in 1885 through to the laying of the Pacific Great Eastern into the Cariboo some thirty years later, brought in new people and helped to establish Kamloops, Ashcroft, and Williams Lake as service centres. The railways had considerable impact on the narrow valleys through which they passed, but fostered nothing like the expansion of settlement that came with railways across the Prairies. Central British Columbia was largely an area through which the trains passed, carrying lumber to the growing markets on the Prairies and grain to tidewater.

The through-railways facilitated some agricultural settlement, notably an attempt to establish a community of English gentlemen farmers along the CPR west of Kamloops, at Walhachin. Where there had been hay and pasture land, orchards were laid out. Unpreparedness for this sort of farming and many serious miscalculations, more so than World War I and the series of natural disasters cited for the tourists on a highway marker, doomed the venture.

By 1900 choice riverside ranchstead sites and reasonably accessible open range throughout the environs of the middle Fraser had been acquired and fenced. New holdings had to be won from the forest. Between the wars, consolidation was noticeable again, a part of the rhythm of British Columbian, and indeed North American, agriculture.

In recent years some ranches have become part-time operations, serving the owners mainly as residences. Jobs in lumbering, or in the commerce and industry of the growing towns, provide the main alternatives. The ranchland itself currently commands very high prices, even where returns from ranching are poor. The buyers, many of them Americans, bring in capital from elsewhere and purchase the land for speculative or recreational as well as ranching purposes. Generally increased taxes raise costs and high land values make expansion difficult for the full-time ranches.

During the interwar years tourist facilities and summer residences appeared here and there, a trend that is accelerating at the present. Many a former cattle ranch is now a guest ranch. The most striking example is the recreational and residential complex being developed on the Cariboo Highway around mile 108 by a Vancouver-based real estate firm. Much business in the smaller towns along the highway is oriented to through traffic, as it was 100 years ago. Cache Creek epitomizes this dependency. The commerce and industry growing out of and serving the region itself can be seen in other towns, most of all in Kamloops, one of the liveliest cities of the interior of British Columbia.

The Okanagan–Shuswap Region

The settlement of the environs of the Okanagan and Shuswap lakes began under an impetus similar to that of regions to the north and west, and was based at first on a similar economy. Under the active promotion of land companies, the Canadian Pacific Railway, and the provincial government, all this changed and the region obtained its distinctive stamp.

Substantial settlement occurred in the Okanagan and the Shuswap in response to the opportunity to grow some of the food needed in the gold diggings to the north. Cattle ranching spread from Shuswap Lake southward to the American border. From Vernon to Sicamous wheat was grown and milled for a few years, but this was rendered uneconomic by the drop in goldfield markets and production on the Prairies. Wheat was replaced by mixed farming and eventually by a limited specialization in dairying.

The inauguration of steamer service on Lake Okanagan in 1886 and the completion of the Shuswap and Okanagan Railway southward from the main line of the Canadian Pacific Railway to Okanagan Lake in 1892 spurred agriculture and settlement. Land companies purchased many of the Okanagan ranches, then subdivided and sold them for the development of orchards. Few people with capital could be enticed into the Shuswap, an area that must have already seemed marginal to the more discerning of the time.

The land companies and the Canadian Pacific Railway advertised Okanagan land in the United Kingdom in glowing terms, attracting people with considerable capital but with very little agricultural skill. As a result many orchards were laid out unwisely in valleys with poor connections to main transportation routes and to good sources of irrigation water. A location too far north meant heavy losses by frost. Planting the wrong varieties of fruit or mismanaging finances could also spell disaster. The net result in many cases was abandonment.

Irrigation, a great asset to ranching and agriculture in the Okanagan Valley from the beginning of settlement, and an absolute prerequisite for orchards later, was first introduced in the late 1860s. The first systems were constructed and maintained by private individuals but eventually some co-operative schemes were devised. The land companies usually constructed irrigation facilities for their own subdivisions. In time irrigation companies were established and shares in a distribution system sold to the farmer.

In spite of initial handicaps and continuing problems, the quiet-spoken and well-read fruit ranchers of the Okanagan Valley were able to achieve a fundamental change in the agriculture of the valley from the United States border to the limit imposed by killing frosts just north of Vernon (Ormsby 1958, p. 440). The establishment of this specialized agriculture, a complement to that of the Prairie Provinces, together with eventual experimentation in controlled marketing, may be considered the unique contribution of this valley and indeed of the province to Canadian agriculture (Ormsby 1945, p. 11).

Settlement and agriculture in the Shuswap did not develop along the same advantageous lines. Some courageous and hard-working people tried to make a go of it, but a combination of poor land, little capital, lack of 'know how,' heavy timber, homesteads that were too small because they had been intended for orchards, and distance from markets made for a tenuous agricultural economy. When all other even vaguely promising agricultural land in the Shuswap region had been taken up people began to squat on forested land leased by the government for logging, over the protests of the logging companies. These 'timber berths' were redefined to validate the settlers' land claims. Among the squatters were many 'restless, inadequate people, sustained by their unrealistic faith that they would succeed, if only they could find the right place' (Akrigg 1964, p. 51).

The three main cities of the Okanagan-Shuswap region, Penticton, Kelowna, and Vernon, owe their origins to different stimuli, but now share several functions. Kelowna was the first permanent settlement of the valley, established soon after the Gold Rush, near a mission. It became a service and processing centre for the surrounding fruit-farming country, and attracted lumber-mills as well. Its urban functions have expanded across the lake toward Westbank where a group of light industries have been established. Vernon was laid out by a land development company in 1892, the year in which the first orchard was planted in the valley. The city has various fruit and vegetable packing plants now, several wood-processing industries, and a major dairy. The village of Penticton began in the 1860s on the alluvial fans where Indians camped in prehistoric times. It became the southern terminus of lake steamers in 1892 and a divisional point on the Kettle Valley Railway in 1915. It now shares in the processing, packing, and distribution of fruit.

The entire valley, with its fairly mild winters, early warm springs, and hot summers, with its facilities for summer and winter sports, its urban amenities, and its good roads to the metropolis on the coast, increasingly attracts tourists. The agricultural potential of the Okanagan is, however, clouded. There are possibilities for expanding irrigation acreages but lack of markets and high production costs limit these prospects. Labour problems and a great deal of through traffic have made it advisable for farmers from one end of the valley to the other to hang out invitations to 'pick your own.' Many orchards are now little more than sidelines for their owners, as well as pleasant places to live.

Agricultural prospects are even poorer for the Shuswap region, with its climatic strictures, and its very limited extent of agricultural land. However, the Shuswap too is increasingly attractive to summer residents and tourists, and many businesses have been established to serve them. This development was facilitated by the completion in 1962 of the Trans-Canada Highway through Rogers Pass. The beauties of the attenuated lake and its surrounding mountains have at last become a sustaining resource.

The Kootenay Region
White men were first attracted to the Kootenay region, as to other parts of the province, by gold-bearing gravels. The exhaustion of these placer deposits was followed by a hiatus in mining during which a few settlers came in to establish farms. It was lode gold, together with lead, zinc, and coal, that eventually became the main economic support of settlement.

The discoveries were made in 1880, and the basic settlement and transportation pattern of the region dates from the mining boom that followed. Mining towns, more accurately described as camps in their early years, sprang up in quick succession. A smelter was operating in Trail in 1897. The CPR eventually acquired it and formed the Consolidated Mining and Smelting Company in 1906. In the succeeding years the fortunes of the mining industry fluctuated in response to market conditions for copper and gold and the exhaustion of ore bodies. The net trend was downward, and many of the mining camps became ghost towns.

In the meantime close ties were being established south of the border.

The gold miners banked or spent their gold in San Francisco during the winters. The cattle required to begin herds had to be driven from the south. Much of the capital that went into the development of the region during its second and more important mining boom of the late 1880s and 1890s was American, and many of the merchants in the new towns were Americans. All of this raised fears of American domination or even annexation. The Dewdney trail had been cut from the Wild Horse River gold-fields to Hope in the 1860s to forestall this southward orientation, but its condition during the winter of each year and the lack of bridges limited its usefulness severely.

The need for better eastern and western links was finally met during the railway building boom that accompanied and continued on from the second surge in mining. The first railway lines ran north-south, but by 1900 the Canadian Pacific Crowsnest line provided a link eastward. The westward link to Vancouver, the Kettle Valley line, was not complete for another 15 years.

With the boom in mining and the coming of the railways, sawmills flourished. There was a demand for mine props and railroad ties, for milled lumber to build the stations and enlarge the towns. In addition a market was developing on the Prairies. During the construction of the CPR's main line, Revelstoke and Golden became sawmilling and supply centres. With its completion they remained as divisional points. Other smaller mill-towns were left as ghost towns when railway construction was finished. Eventually the lumber industry was revitalized along more modern lines.

The history of agriculture, and indeed the entire Kootenay economy from the lapse of the second mining boom early in the twentieth century to the interwar years, is a rather dreary one. By the eve of World War II population had declined from earlier highs. Agriculture was precarious mainly because of poor access to markets, the small size of many farms, and poor farming practices. Farm abandonment, consolidation, shifts to more extensive mixed farming, and a search for supplemental employment were the results.

Attempts at settlement promotion did not go too well. Land companies advertised their holdings in the Kootenays as suitable for dairies and orchards, which was ill-advised and not too successful. Nevertheless some settlers of Anglo-Saxon background took up land, becoming the area's gentlemen farmers.

The arrival of Doukhobors from 1910 to 1920 was initially very promising. They were just what the area needed, a stable European peasant population. These people were dissidents of the Russian Orthodox Church who had moved onto homesteads in Saskatchewan in 1899. About ten years later, the more dissatisfied of the prairie Doukhobors decided to buy land in southeastern British Columbia where they hoped they would find the isolation and freedom for an Utopian community. A minority of the Kootenay Doukhobors, in turn, became the radical and very troublesome 'Sons of Freedom.'

Initially the Doukhobors lived on large communal farms scattered between Grand Forks and Nelson. The headquarters of the Christian Community of Universal Brotherhood, the organization by means of which they had bought their land on credit and communally managed their economic affairs, was in Brilliant. Mismanagement, disaffection in favour of individual farm management, and the poor economic conditions of the thirties brought the collapse of the organization and foreclosure on the gigantic mortgage in 1939. To forestall severe hardship, the provincial government satisfied the creditors and assumed control of Doukhobor lands. Some have since purchased their land, and others are tenants of the government, paying nominal rents. The derelict buildings of the old communal farms remain as curiosities in the cultural landscape.

One bright spot in the whole agricultural picture has been a reclamation project on the Kootenay Flats near Creston. After several false starts from 1885 onward, the scheme got underway in the 1930s and now has 25,000 acres reclaimed, most of it under cereals.

Following World War II the construction of good roads, improvement of irrigation facilities, introduction of new crops, and other innovations have enhanced the general agricultural picture considerably. Firmer prospects have also appeared for mining, forestry, hydroelectric power, pulp and paper, and tourism, bringing some revival to the towns.

The remote parts of the Kootenays, particularly around Slocan Lake and the northern arm of Kootenay Lake, are currently attractive to Canadians and Americans who are turning their backs on cities and many other aspects of modern North American life. They have settled as single families and in communes away from the main roads. Once again, this region is of interest to Utopians.

The North Central Region

As one moves northward, the beginnings of substantial settlement are more recent. The settlement of North Central British Columbia received its first impetus in the late 1860s from the construction of a section of the telegraph line that was to link the eastern United States with Europe via Alaska and Siberia. Construction and operating crews settled along the line and the right of way subsequently provided a means of access for agricultural settlers. Only in 1871, after placer gold mining had waned elsewhere in the province, was the metal discovered in the gravels of the Omineca River, northeast of the present town of Smithers. Gold seekers began to come into the region via the Skeena River. Farms were established along this route to serve the needs of the miners, and Hazelton developed into a supply centre.

By 1908 a road had been completed through the Skeena and Bulkley river valleys from Terrace to Telkwa. It had been preceded and was followed by agricultural settlers obtaining land through homesteading or purchase. At this time settlers were also moving by river into the 'Lake District' of the Nechako River headwaters, southwest of Fort Fraser. So far the entry of settlers had been mainly from the west.

The building of the Grand Trunk Pacific Railway, later the Canadian National, was begun in 1907 and finished in 1914. It initiated a short but lively boom, which was dampened by World War I. Small sawmills were set up in scattered locations along the route to make ties. A few farms were established in areas made more accessible by the railway, such as the Nechako valley and the shores of Francois and Ootsa lakes. Vigorous speculation was set off around the Fort George fur trading post, which soon became a small town and took on the name of Prince George. A city of grandiose proportions and design, to be called Prince Rupert, was planned as the western terminal. For various reasons related to its meagre immediate hinterland and its disadvantageous situation relative to southern ports, it never did become the port that the railway hoped would rival Vancouver. It is now a modest city of about 16,000 people, dependent on shipping, fishing, and a nearby pulp and paper mill.

The independent choice of farm location by early homesteaders led to dispersed settlement throughout North Central British Columbia. To prevent excessive dispersion of settlement, to curb speculation, and to ensure that land was used for more than just the exploitation of wood, the provincial government restricted development early in this century by levying a tax on non-cultivated land within farms, and tightened regulations on homesteads. This eventually resulted in loose agglomerations tied to the railway, from which most of the bread-winners obtained part-time or full-time employment.

The Canadian National Railway had established a Department of Colonization with headquarters in Prince George by 1913. Within the next 40 years the company brought in more than 1000 families of various ethnic groups, particularly Swiss and Dutch, who were added to a population mainly of British origin. In the early 1940s several dozen Mennonite families from Saskatchewan settled in the 'Lake District' as well as in the vicinity of Vanderhoof; they were near other Mennonites who had already moved into the area in the 1920s, but were dispersed among people of varied cultural background. The cultural background of the population in North Central British Columbia is quite heterogenous and has left few distinctive impressions on the landscape.

The most remarkable recent urban growth in the region is noticeable in Prince George, a city of about 33,000 in 1971. Basic to that growth have been the completion of the John Hart Highway to Dawson Creek in 1952, the building of the Pacific Great Eastern Railway to Prince George in the same year and its later extension to the Peace River, the expansion of lumber-milling, the recent development of pulp-milling and a petrochemical industry. It is now the most important service centre for North–Central British Columbia. It still has about it the lingering atmosphere of a 'boom town,' but at the same time boasts an increasingly varied and sophisticated array of services. Some specific aspects of its economic growth are discussed in Chapter 4.

Expansion of agricultural land as well as improvement in agricultural technology on existing farms is being retarded in North–Central British Columbia by off-farm job opportunities, particularly in forestry, as well as transportation facilities that allow commuting. As elsewhere in the province, very much of the farming is part-time. This seems uneconomic unless one considers the amenities of rural residence. A visual indication of such a situation is the combination of a well-kept house with deteriorating outbuildings.

Nevertheless, there is new agricultural land available, set in attractive wooded hill country, favoured by a moderate climate, and surrounded by recreational opportunities. Farmland prices have risen in this region, as in neighbouring regions, reflecting a lively demand. However, the words 'pioneer' and 'frontier' seem hardly applicable now. The newcomer may be a European immigrant on his way to better things in the city; more often he is an American or Canadian bringing capital saved outside and seeking a speculative investment or a retreat.

There is a great deal of interest in, and perhaps something of a provincial mystique about, the development of the north-central interior. In large part, it is a very modern response to the aesthetic quality of the landscape and its recreational potential, as well as to the prospects for continued industrialization and general economic growth.

The Peace River Region
The Peace River country of British Columbia was the last major region of the province to be occupied, except for the still essentially empty northwest. Fur traders arrived in the early years of the 19th century, mission-

aries by the 1880s, and then gold seekers, distracted on their way to the Klondike, just before the turn of the century. On the basis of the eastward penetration of the prospectors and British colonial justice, the provincial boundary was drawn along the 120° meridian from about 54° N latitude instead of continuing along the crest of the Rockies.

The British Columbia section of the Peace River country was settled in the early years of the twentieth century, slightly later than the Alberta section. The settlers came from the east in horse-drawn wagons and on foot along trails extending westward and northwestward from the successive ends of the railway. They generally took up land by homesteading. The resulting settlement pattern was extremely dispersed, in spite of the fact that many of the settlers arrived in groups with distinct cultural backgrounds. Government land policy, which dictated that a residence should be established on each homestead, made village settlement impossible. The broken topography and a great variety of soils dispersed the farms even further. This scattering made life rather lonely, particularly during the long, cold winters or in wet weather when all roads and trails softened into a gluelike mud.

In 1939 the Canadian Colonization Association, a subsidiary of the CNR, settled some 1000 Sudetan Germans in the Tupper Creek district, just south of Pouce Coupe. This developed into one of the most successful colonization schemes in Canada. After World War II many returning soldiers settled in the Peace River country, aided by government cash grants, training schemes, and long-term payment plans. They helped to fill out the existing settlement pattern rather than to extend its periphery.

After a lag during the 1950s, the alienation of crown lands and activity on the private real estate market increased again, a trend which has continued to the present. This demand for land, however, reflects not only an interest in farming and ranching, but the promise of profits and jobs in forestry, oil or gas, as well as the speculative value of land along the main highways. The Peace River country can perhaps still be called an 'active frontier' (Vanderhill 1963, p. 39), but what goes on hardly fits the usual concept of 'pioneering.'

Isolation was the main early problem of the Albertan as well as British Columbian sections of the Peace River region. It was ameliorated for the western section first by the railway from Edmonton and then by the Alaska Highway, both of which oriented the region eastward, which was undesirable from British Columbia's point of view. This eastward orientation has been diminished but not overcome by the completion of the John Hart Highway in 1952, the extension of the Pacific Great Eastern Railway to

Dawson Creek and Fort St John in 1958 and its extension beyond to Fort Nelson in 1971, and by the construction of new oil and gas pipelines to the southwest coast.

In many ways the process and form of British Columbia's settlement present only variations on western Canadian or western North American themes. Most of the factors that moulded the cultural landscapes, some of historical interest now, others still operative, have been felt in one way or another throughout the North American West, particularly in the Cordillera. The grid pattern of land subdivision is general, as is the related dispersal of rural settlement. Houses have traditionally been, and still are, mainly of wood – from the log cabin to the suburban frame bungalow. House and barn styles have been freely copied back and forth over great distances. The fretwork, gables, dormer windows, and porches brought from older parts of North America are not very informative of the culture of the inhabitants except in rare cases. Reading the impact of the culture on the landscape is not so much a matter of deciphering ethnic peculiarities as of finding western expressions of very broad North American cultural traits and general processes of cultural change.

The traditional expansionist meaning of the word 'settlement' as a process still applies in parts of British Columbia. More interesting is the reorientation of settlement patterns and farms, particularly the ever tightening integration of farms, towns, and cities, and the increasing focus of the entire province on its southwestern corner.

3 Physiography and Hydrology of Six River Basins

H. OLAV SLAYMAKER

Flows of water and sediment in the six major river basins of British Columbia show varied responses to land surface and atmospheric processes within the basins. Comprehensive data on such flows would provide spatial integrators of the full range of physical processes operating to degrade or aggrade the landscape at the present time, but, unfortunately, available records are often far from comprehensive. In this chapter it will therefore be necessary, at times, to make inferences from the scattered records, particularly in discussing some of the northern rivers. Two regional entities will be used in the discussions: first the river basin, because the data on flows of water and sediment that are available commonly refer to such a spatial unit, and secondly the physiographic region, which provides greater hydrologic homogeneity than the river basin. Most of the physiographic regions are smaller than the river basins, making it possible to consider smaller-scale processes.

The six major river basins to be discussed are those of the Fraser, Columbia, Peace, Liard, Stikine, and Skeena (Figure 3.1 and Table 3.1). The combined area of these basins is about 713,000 square kilometres, of which about 80 per cent lies at an elevation greater than 1000 metres. Because the great majority of the meteorological and hydrometric stations of the province are located below the 1000-metre level a high priority is currently being placed on research activities in the alpine and sub-alpine zones. Particular mention should be made of research under the direction of the Meteorological Service, Canada Department of the Environment, the Canada Land Inventory, the Glaciology Division and Surface Water Survey of the Inland Waters Branch, the International Hydrologic Decade, the International Biological Programme, and the University of British Columbia. Until the data from these research projects are collated, however, reliance must be placed on extrapolated data for the high-altitude areas. The map of mean annual precipitation (Figure 3.2), for example, brings out clearly the four major physiographic subdivisions of British

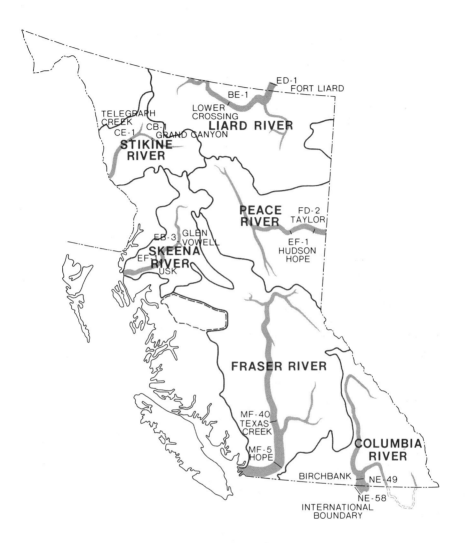

ED-1
FORT LIARD
BE-1
LOWER
CROSSING
TELEGRAPH
CREEK
CB-1
CE-1
GRAND CANYON
**STIKINE
RIVER**

LIARD RIVER

**PEACE
RIVER**
FD-2
TAYLOR

EB-3
GLEN
VOWELL
EF-1
HUDSON
HOPE

EF
**SKEENA
RIVER**
USK

FRASER RIVER

MF-40
TEXAS
CREEK

MF-5
HOPE

**COLUMBIA
RIVER**

BIRCHBANK
NE-49

NE-58
INTERNATIONAL
BOUNDARY

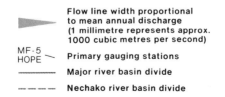

Flow line width proportional
to mean annual discharge
(1 millimetre represents approx.
1000 cubic metres per second)

MF-5
HOPE   Primary gauging stations

———   Major river basin divide

- - - -   Nechako river basin divide

**3.1
Six Major River Basins – Mean Annual Discharge**

Table 3.1 The six major river basins of British Columbia

Basin	Area in B.C. (sq. km.)	Estimated mean discharge (c.m.s.)	Area gauged (sq. km.)	Mean discharge gauged (c.m.s.)	
Fraser	233,000 (219,000)[1]	3751	217,000[2] (203,000)[1]	2704	(1912–67)
Columbia	102,000	2262	88,000[3]	2019	(1913–67)
Peace	128,000	1738	99,000[4]	1470	(1951–67)
Liard	144,000	1536	222,000[5]	1846	(1966–8)
Stikine	51,000	1492	29,000[6]	368	(1965–8)
Skeena	54,000	1699	39,000[7]	903	(1936–67)

1 Drainage area reduced by completion of Kenney Dam (October 1952).
2 Fraser River at Hope.
3 Columbia River at Trail (1914–36); at Birchbank (1938–67).
4 Peace River near Taylor.
5 Liard River at Fort Liard, Northwest Territories.
6 Stikine River at Telegraph Creek.
7 Skeena River at Usk.

Columbia, largely because the map was compiled on the basis of inferred relationships between altitude, relief, and precipitation.

The eighteen physiographic regions to be discussed are itemized on Figure 3.3 and in Table 3.2 (after Holland 1964). They are subdivisions of the four major physiographic entities of British Columbia, which, from west to east, are known as the Western System of the Cordilleran Region, the Interior System of the Cordilleran Region, the Eastern System of the Cordilleran Region, and the Interior Plains. The Western System, which includes the Coast Mountains, is characterized by massive plutonic rock bodies or by folded volcanic and sedimentary strata intruded by scattered plutons, all of which have produced high-relief and high-altitude terrain. The Interior System is made of folded sedimentary and volcanic rocks, metamorphic rocks, all intruded by scattered plutons, with local areas of flat-lying volcanic strata; intermediate altitudes and low relief are more characteristic of this terrain. The Eastern System is formed almost exclusively of folded sedimentary strata and forms high-altitude, high-relief terrain. The Interior Plains, which occupy the area between the Rocky Mountains and the Canadian Shield, in British Columbia are underlain by Cretaceous sedimentary rocks and form low-relief, intermediate-altitude terrain. These four physiographic systems control the pattern of climate, vegetation, and hydrology in British Columbia.

With this general introduction in mind, one can now turn to the more detailed physiographic subdivisions of the province.

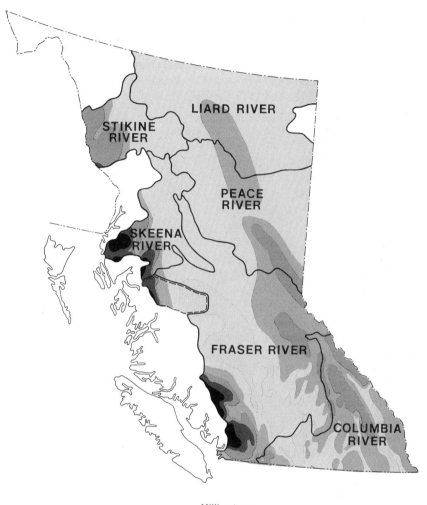

LIARD RIVER

STIKINE
RIVER

PEACE
RIVER

SKEENA
RIVER

FRASER RIVER

COLUMBIA
RIVER

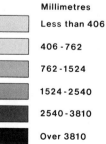

Millimetres

Less than 406

406 - 762

762 - 1524

1524 - 2540

2540 - 3810

Over 3810

3.2
Six Major River Basins – Mean Annual Precipitation
(from Canada Land Inventory, ARDA, Map No. 17)

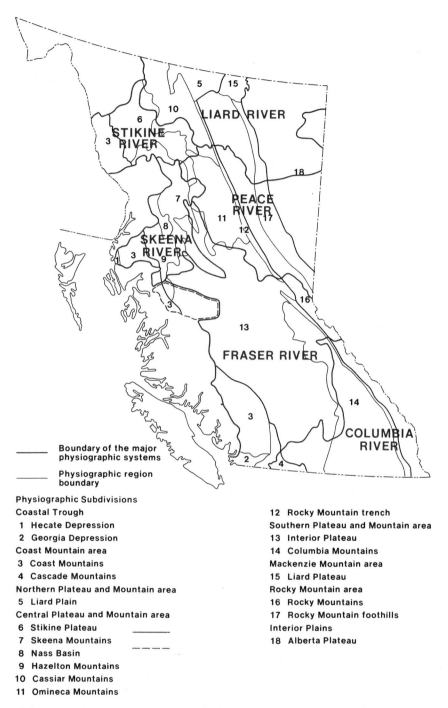

Boundary of the major
physiographic systems

Physiographic region
boundary

Physiographic Subdivisions
Coastal Trough
 1 Hecate Depression
 2 Georgia Depression
Coast Mountain area
 3 Coast Mountains
 4 Cascade Mountains
Northern Plateau and Mountain area
 5 Liard Plain
Central Plateau and Mountain area
 6 Stikine Plateau
 7 Skeena Mountains
 8 Nass Basin
 9 Hazelton Mountains
 10 Cassiar Mountains
 11 Omineca Mountains

 12 Rocky Mountain trench
Southern Plateau and Mountain area
 13 Interior Plateau
 14 Columbia Mountains
Mackenzie Mountain area
 15 Liard Plateau
Rocky Mountain area
 16 Rocky Mountains
 17 Rocky Mountain foothills
Interior Plains
 18 Alberta Plateau

3.3
Six Major River Basins – Physiographic Regions

Table 3.2   The eighteen physiographic regions of British Columbia's major river basins

Physiographic region	Area (sq. km.)	Mean discharge (c.m.s./sq.km.)
Western System		
Hecate Depression	500	0.066
Georgia Depression	2,300	0.021
Coast Mountains	50,500	0.069
Cascade Mountains	6,700	0.035
	60,000	0.063
Interior System		
Liard Plain	11,700	0.011
Stikine Plateau	30,600	0.011
Skeena Mountains	22,000	0.022
Nass Basin	3,600	0.029
Hazelton Mountains	14,000	0.025
Cassiar Mountains	38,800	0.015
Omineca Mountains	33,700	0.018
Interior Plateau	191,800	0.005
Columbia Mountains	75,600	0.031
Rocky Mountain Trench	5,200	0.008
	427,000	0.014
Eastern System		
Liard Plateau	7,100	0.011
Rocky Mountains	90,700	0.031
Rocky Mountain Foothills	24,600	0.014
	122,400	0.026
Interior Plains		
Alberta Plateau	103,600	0.005

MAJOR PHYSIOGRAPHIC REGIONS

Coastal Trough (including Hecate and Georgia Depressions)

The Coastal Trough physiographic region is represented in two of the major river basins of British Columbia by 500 square kilometres around the estuary of the Skeena and by 2300 square kilometres around the delta of the Fraser. These areas are known as the Hecate and Georgia depressions respectively, and they form parts of the continuous low-lying area separating the mountains of Vancouver Island and the Queen Charlotte Islands from the Coast Mountains.

So small is the area occupied by the Hecate Depression in the Skeena basin that it is not important hydrologically. The Georgia Depression, on the other hand, has its own distinctive hydrology, which, although it does not influence the flow of the Fraser significantly, influences several rivers tributary to the Fraser.

Within the Georgia Depression, there are two distinct subregions known as the Georgia Lowland and the Fraser Lowland. The former is dominantly erosional and is thought to contain remnants of a Tertiary erosion surface, and the latter is dominantly a depositional environment. The cuestas of the Lower Mainland of British Columbia, such as Burnaby Mountain, form a part of the Georgia Lowland, and on them superficial unconsolidated deposits are thin and in general impermeable. Runoff is rapid and groundwater storage is small. The unconsolidated glacial, glacio-marine, fluvio-glacial, and fluvial deposits with depths of 600 metres and more are a part of the Fraser Lowland. Important aquifers such as outwash sand and gravel and fluvial sand and gravel trapped between stony clays are typical of this area; because less than 7 per cent of the mean annual precipitation of 762–1524 millimetres falls during July and August, extensive use is made of the groundwater for domestic purposes in communities south of the Fraser River.

Hydrometric data from one station[1] with its drainage area entirely within the Georgia Depression show a mean discharge intensity of 0.021 c.m.s. per square kilometre (or about 660 millimetres mean annual runoff). The most interesting feature of the discharge regime is its domination by the winter (December–January) rains peak and the very low discharges recorded during the months of July and August. This is the only physiographic region in any of the six major river basins where snowmelt discharge is of entirely minor significance. The region records the smallest quantities of snowfall (less than 10 per cent of the mean annual precipitation) and the longest crop growing season (up to 270 days) of any part of the provincial mainland.

Coast Mountains

About 28,500 square kilometres of the Coast Mountains physiographic region is in the Fraser basin, about 9000 square kilometres in the Skeena basin, and about 13,000 square kilometres in the Stikine basin. The three parts correspond approximately to three distinctive subregions of the Coast Mountains known respectively as the Pacific, Kitimat, and Boundary ranges. The Pacific Ranges are characterized by peaks in the 3000–

1   Sumas River near Huntingdon (8MH-29), 149 sq. km., 1952–67.

3400 metre range and by extensive glacierization, especially at the heads of the Bridge and Lillooet River valleys. Glacier mass budget studies representative of the Pacific Ranges are in progress at Sentinel and Place glaciers (Stanley 1970; Ostrem 1966a, b). The peaks of the Kitimat Ranges, by contrast, rarely exceed 2600 metres above sea level and there are no extensive ice-fields. The most spectacular peaks associated with the most extensive glacierization are seen in the Boundary Ranges, and work in progress on the Berendon Glacier is thought to provide representative hydrologic data for this region (Stanley 1970).

These mountain ranges form a massive barrier to Pacific and Arctic maritime air masses which are forced to ascend and in so doing are cooled and lose their moisture as heavy precipitation. As a result, this physiographic region has the greatest untapped water resources and records some of the highest instantaneous discharge intensities in the whole of Canada. The Seymour River, for example, reached 623 c.m.s. at 8 p.m. on 26 November 1949, at a point where it drains 176 square kilometres.

The Coast Mountains are formed mainly of foliated and non-foliated granitoid rocks, but extensive areas of metamorphic rocks are also present. In the Pacific and Boundary ranges there is the added complication of Pleistocene and Recent vulcanism, which has given rise to some distinctively spirelike peaks. In general it can be said that the highest peaks and ridges of the Coast Mountains are more serrate and jagged than those of the Rocky Mountains. This is partly because these Coast peaks were nunataks during the last glacial advance and partly (in the case of the Tantalus Range in the Pacific Ranges for example) a result of localized metamorphic lithology.

Hydrometric data for six stations[2] in the Coast Mountains show a mean discharge intensity of 0.069 c.m.s. per square kilometre (or about 2180 millimetres mean annual runoff). In all these discharge hydrographs there are two clear peaks, one corresponding to the snowmelt peak in May-June and the other the fall rains peak in September-October. In the Boundary and Pacific ranges, a third distinct peak associated with the glacial melt peak is discernible in July-August.

Cascade Mountains

About 4500 square kilometres of the Cascade Mountains physiographic region is in the Fraser and Skagit basins and 2200 square kilometres in

---

2 Birkenhead River at Mount Currie (8MG-8), 596 sq. km., 1945–67; Cayoosh Creek near Lillooet (8ME-2), 906 sq. km., 1958–60 and 1963–7; Exchamsiks River near Terrace (8EG-12), 376 sq. km., 1962–7; Lillooet River near Pemberton (8MG-5), 2070 sq. km., 1923–67; Norrish Creek near Dewdney (8MH-58), 114 sq. km., 1959–67; Unuk River near Stewart (8DD-1), 1515 sq. km., 1960, 1961, and 1966–7.

the Columbia basin. The Cascade Mountains are separated from the Coast Mountains by the Fraser River canyon and are divided into the Skagit, Hozameen, and Okanagan ranges. Peaks are between 2400 and 2700 metres, and whereas those of the Skagit and Hozameen ranges are characteristically serrate, the peaks of the Okanagan Range are more rounded in form. Strongly folded and metamorphosed sediments and volcanics and granite intrusions make up the dominant lithologies in the Cascade Mountains. Mean annual precipitation is high, particularly in the Skagit and southern part of the Hozameen ranges where it exceeds 1524 millimetres. The northern part of the Hozameen Range, which lies in the rain shadow of the Coast Mountains, and also the Okanagan Range receive between 762 and 1524 millimetres mean annual precipitation. Hydrometric data from six stations[3] indicate a mean discharge intensity of 0.035 c.m.s. per square kilometre (or about 1100 millimetres mean annual runoff) for the Cascade Mountains in British Columbia. On the eastern slopes of the mountains there is only one major discharge peak per year associated with the snowmelt period of May-June. On the western side, the fall and winter rains of October and December give rise to a second high discharge period which may be responsible for major flooding problems in the steep-sided mountain valleys.

Liard Plain and Stikine Plateau
Of the 42,300 square kilometres represented by these two physiographic regions, 26,000 is in the Stikine River basin and 13,000 in the Liard River basin. The remaining 3300 square kilometres is in the Skeena and Peace River basins. The area is little known climatologically or hydrologically, but the work of Mathews (1947) has directed attention to the volcanic landforms of the Stikine Plateau. The surface of the Liard Plain is largely between 800 and 1100 metres above sea level and is a low-relief, till-covered plain, with eskers, drumlins, and morainic features of fresh appearance. Surfaces represented in the Stikine Plateau, by contrast, include the relatively undissected plateau surfaces of the Kawdy, Nahlin, Klastline, and Spatsizi plateaus, the flat-topped, steep-sided volcanoes called tuyas of the Kawdy Plateau, the shield volcano of Level Mountain in the Nahlin Plateau, the moderately dissected plateau surface of the Tanzilla

---

3 Chilliwack River at Vedder Crossing (8MH-1), 1254 sq. km., 1916–31 and 1951–67; Coquihalla River near Hope (8MF-3), 932 sq. km., 1914–22 and 1959–67; Slesse Creek near Vedder Crossing (8MH-56), 162 sq. km., 1957–67; Silverhope Creek near Hope (8MF-9), 207 sq. km., 1964–7; Ashnola River near Keremeos (8NL-4), 1035 sq. km., 1947–67; Tulameen River at Princeton (8NL-24), 1760 sq. km., 1950–67.

Plateau, the extremely dissected Tahltan Highlands, and the complex volcanic cone of Mount Edziza in the Tahltan Highlands. The Stikine Plateau is thus a highly heterogeneous region, and it is probable that it is equally variable climatically and hydrologically. No significance should be attached to the impression of homogeneity gained from the mean annual precipitation map (Figure 3.2) other than the fact that there are only two rain gauges (Telegraph Creek and Dease Lake) in the region.

Hydrometric data from one station[4] indicate a mean discharge intensity of 0.011 c.m.s. per square kilometre (or about 350 millimetres mean annual runoff). The highest flows of the year are associated with the May-June snowmelt peak, but there is also evidence of recurring high flows in October as a response to fall rains. These fall flows are on the average very minor in comparison with the snowmelt floods, but in individual years they may be troublesome.

Cassiar, Omineca, Skeena, and Hazelton Mountains

These four physiographic regions occupy 108,500 square kilometres of the northern part of British Columbia's major river basins: 31,000 in the Skeena basin, 11,300 in the Stikine basin, 4700 in the Fraser basin, 29,000 in the Liard basin, and 32,500 in the Peace basin. The Cassiar Mountains, which extend from the Yukon border to the Finlay River, are the most continental and so the driest of these mountain regions. The region contains four distinctive subdivisions known as the Dease Plateau and the Stikine, Sifton, and Kechika ranges. The so-called Cassiar batholith forms the geologic core of the region, an area of granitic rocks intruded into older sedimentary and volcanic rocks. Quartzite, limestone, and gneiss are the major peak formers. Hydrometric data from three stations[5] indicate a mean discharge intensity of 0.015 c.m.s. per square kilometre (or about 470 millimetres mean annual runoff). A June snowmelt peak is well developed on the northeastern slopes of these mountains, and on the southwestern slopes a minor fall peak is present.

Perhaps the least well known region in the province is the Omineca Mountains. Structurally they consist of a core of granitic rocks surrounded by older metamorphics and volcanics. There are three generally recognized subdivisions known as the Swannell, Finlay, and Hogem ranges. Hydrometric data from one station[6] indicate a mean discharge in-

---

4 Tuya River near Telegraph Creek (8CD-1), 3522 sq. km., 1962–7.

5 Dease River at McDame (10AC-2), 6990 sq. km., 1962–7; Blue River near mouth (10AC-4), 1730 sq. km., 1964–7; Cottonwood River above Bass Creek (10AC-5), 888 sq. km., 1964–7.

6 Omineca River near Germansen Landing (7EC-1), 5076 sq. km., 1960–7.

tensity of 0.018 c.m.s. per square kilometre (or about 570 millimetres mean annual runoff). From this one record it appears that the June snow-melt peak is dominant and fall rains do not greatly influence the discharge regime.

The Skeena Mountains are located to the west of the Cassiar and Omineca mountains and are consequently more humid. Hydrometric data from one station[7] indicate a mean discharge intensity of 0.022 c.m.s. per square kilometre (or about 690 millimetres mean annual runoff). Both a May-June snowmelt peak and a September-October peak are well developed in the record. Very complex and tightly folded sedimentary rocks, dominantly argillite, shale, and graywacke, underly the region. The peaks and ridges are commonly serrate, indicating intense alpine glaciation during the Pleistocene.

The Hazelton Mountains are to the south and west of the Skeena Mountains, and according to the evidence of four hydrometric stations[8] have a mean discharge intensity of 0.025 c.m.s. per square kilometre (or about 790 millimetres mean annual runoff). The region contains four major ranges known as the Nass Ranges to the north of the Skeena River, the Bulkley Ranges to the south, the Kispiox Range rising out of the Nass Basin as an outlier from the main mass of the Hazelton Mountains, and the Tahtsa Ranges in the northwestern extremity of the Fraser River basin. Composed of sedimentary and volcanic rocks which are intruded by isolated stocks, these ranges have jagged peaks up to 2800 metres above sea level.

Nass Basin and the Rocky Mountain Trench
These two low-relief regions of the Interior System provide interesting contrasts in climate and hydrology. The Nass basin, occupying 3600 square kilometres in the Skeena River basin, is an area of low relief below 800 metres and is bounded by the Coast, Skeena, and Hazelton mountains. Its most interesting feature is that it is affected by incursions of maritime air masses. Hydrometric data from one station[9] indicate a mean discharge intensity of 0.029 c.m.s per square kilometre (or about 910 millimetres mean annual runoff), and the dense Coast Forest vegetation is evidence of the biotic response to greater humidity.

7   Klappan River near Telegraph Creek (8CC-1), 3522 sq. km., 1962–7.
8   Bulkley River at Quick (8EE-4), 7250 sq. km., 1945–67; Goathorn Creek near Telkwa (8EE-8), 132 sq. km., 1960–7; Kitseguecla River near Skeena Crossing (8EE-4), 816 sq. km., 1960–7; Zymoetz River above O.K. Creek (8EF-5), 2850 sq. km., 1963–7.
9   Kispiox River near Hazelton (8EB-4), 1854 sq. km., 1963–7.

The Rocky Mountain Trench is a spectacular topographic feature which extends northwestward from the 49th parallel almost to the Liard River, a distance of some 1400 kilometres. The width of the Trench ranges from 3 to 15 kilometres, and it is drained successively northwestwards by the Kootenay, Columbia, and Canoe rivers (1800 square kilometres), the Fraser River (800 square kilometres), the Parsnip and Finlay rivers (2000 square kilometres), and the Kechika River (600 square kilometres). The area is extremely dry, with a mean discharge[10] intensity of 0.008 c.m.s. per square kilometre (or about 250 millimetres of mean annual runoff), but progressively less arid towards the north.

Interior Plateau
This is the largest physiographic region in the province. It covers about 191,800 square kilometres, of which 162,000 is in the Fraser River basin, 15,000 in the Columbia River basin, 10,000 in the Skeena River basin, and about 4800 in the Peace River basin. The western half of the region contains plateau and basin areas known as the Fraser Basin, the Nechako Plateau, the Fraser Plateau, and the Thompson Plateau. The eastern half, by contrast, is made up of the upland areas of the Quesnel, Shuswap, and Okanagan Highlands. The plateau and basin areas have low relief and range in elevation from 600 to 2100 metres. They have a thick cover of glacial drift and little bed-rock exposure. The plateau surfaces are by no means flat as they have slopes of from 25 to 80 metres per kilometre and local bluffs up to 60 metres high. Shield volcanoes of Miocene age are present in the western part of the plateau but they have little regional impact on either water or sediment flows.

The general climate of the region (Chapman 1952) varies from a humid, continental, cool, short, summer type in the north (for example, the Stuart and Nechako River valleys) to a middle-latitude steppe type in the south (for example, the Thompson and Okanagan River valleys). In spite of this considerable range in climatic type, there are some distinctive features common to the whole region. Among these are low to moderate precipitation (200–500 millimetres per year), a high percentage falling as snow (35–40 per cent), and a wide range of daily and annual temperatures. The growing season, defined in terms of the number of days with a mean daily temperature above 5° C, ranges from 140 in the Takla Lake area to above 230 days in the middle Fraser Valley and the southern Oka-

10   Dry Gulch Creek near Radium Junction (8NA-56), 4 sq. km., 1964–7; Goldie Creek near Invermere (8NA-55), 17.5 sq. km., 1966–7; Windermere Creek near Windermere (8NA-24), 85 sq. km., 1959–67.

nagan. Hydrometric data from six stations[11] in the plateau and basin region of the Interior Plateau indicate a mean discharge intensity of 0.004 c.m.s. per square kilometre (or about 130 millimetres mean annual runoff). There is only one important discharge peak per year and this is the late May–early June snowmelt peak throughout the region. The mapping of precipitation regimes provides little information relevant to runoff regime analysis because rainfall-runoff relationships are so completely dominated by the snowmelt process. Not only is this snowmelt discharge peak important within the Interior Plateau region, it is also the major component in the Fraser River flood discharge in late May–early June at Hope. This area, which provides only 17 per cent of the mean annual discharge of the Fraser River (Table 2.3), may generate as much as 30 per cent of the maximum daily discharge at Hope. An understanding of the snowmelt process and its variations over the area of the Interior Plateau is thus exceedingly important (Quick 1965) in the prediction of flood events in the lower Fraser Valley.

The highland areas of the Interior Plateau can be treated conveniently in a separate paragraph as they are hydrologically and climatically somewhat distinct. They have elevations ranging from 1500 to 2800 metres, have rounded summits, and are more dissected near the Columbia Mountains. Evidence of Pleistocene volcanic activity is locally extensive, but on a regional scale flows of water and sediment are scarcely influenced by the presence of these erodible rocks. The general climate of these highland areas is classified as humid continental, with cool short summers, and nowhere is there a dry season. Mean annual precipitation ranges between 400 and 1250 millimetres, including 150 to 500 centimetres of snow, as compared with the 75 to 200 centimetres of snow in the plateau and basin areas. Hydrometric data from five stations[12] in this part of the Interior Plateau indicate a mean discharge intensity of 0.014 c.m.s. per square kilometre (or about 440 millimetres mean annual runoff). There is only one major discharge peak per year throughout this part of the region and

11 Salmon River near Prince George (8KC-1), 4350 sq. km., 1953–67; Chilako River near Prince George (8JC-5), 3420 sq. km., 1960–7; Salmon River at Falkland (8LE-20), 1030 sq. km., 1951–61 and 1966–7; Deadman River above Criss Creek (8LF-27), 777 sq. km., 1961–7; Bonaparte River near Cache Creek (8LF-60), 3445 sq. km., 1960–7; Nicola River near Merritt (8LG-7), 4660 sq. km., 1957–67.
12 Cale Creek near Red Rock (8KE-15), 160 sq. km., 1956–67; Naver Creek at Hixon (8KE-14), 658 sq. km., 1956–8 and 1963–7; Barriere River at mouth (8LB-20), 1140 sq. km., 1915–30, 1952–8, and 1963–7; Brash Creek near Enderby (8LC-4), 26 sq. km., 1959–67; West Kettle River near McCulloch (8NN-15), 250 sq. km., 1964–7.

it corresponds to the snowmelt peak of May–early June. The mean annual runoff for the whole Interior Plateau physiographic region is about 150 millimetres.

Columbia Mountains

About 57,000 of the 75,600 square kilometres area of the Columbia Mountains is in the Columbia River basin and the remainder lies in the Fraser River basin. There are four constituent ranges which make up this region, namely the Cariboo Mountains to the north and the Monashee, Selkirk, and Purcell mountains from west to east in the southern half of the region. The Cariboo Mountains and the northernmost part of the other ranges are the most rugged and contain extensively glacierized areas, especially around Mount Sir Wilfrid Laurier (3700 metres), Mount Sir Sanford (3600 metres), Mount Dawson (3500 metres), and Mount Farnham (3550 metres). Lithologies range from metamorphic, through sedimentary and volcanic rocks, to granites. In the Cariboo Mountains, quartzite is the principal rock type and the principal ridge former, and in the Monashees, foliated gneisses are widespread. The Selkirk peaks are held up by quartzite and limestone which are relatively resistant to erosion, and the Purcell Mountains have peaks characterized by massiveness when underlain by quartzite and granite and which are spirelike when formed of slates. All these mountain ranges, whether glacierized or not, have been intensely glaciated in the past and form spectacularly beautiful alpine mountain country.

The general climate of the region is alpine humid continental, becoming progressively less humid southwards. Mean annual precipitation ranges from below 500 millimetres around Creston to over 2000 millimetres over the higher areas, with 30 to 40 per cent being in the form of snow. Hydrometric data from seven stations[13] indicate a mean discharge intensity of 0.031 c.m.s. per square kilometre (or about 980 millimetres mean annual runoff), with a significantly higher runoff in the Cariboo Mountains than in the other three ranges. Stations in the Cariboo Mountains and in the northern parts of the other ranges have two prominent discharge peaks corresponding to snow and glacier melt periods and a

13 Spillimacheen River (8NA-11), 1500 sq. km., 1948–67; Downie Creek near Revelstoke (8ND-9), 650 sq. km., 1959–67; Incommapleux River near Beaton (8NE-1), 1000 sq. km., 1952–67; St Mary River near Marysville (8NG-46), 1475 sq. km., 1948–67; Moyie River at Eastport (8NH-6), 1475 sq. km., 1929–67; Goat River near Erickson (8NG-4), 1115 sq. km., 1925–52 and 1955–67; North Thompson River at Birch Island (8LB-47), 4530 sq. km., 1960–7.

minor fall peak. In the southern part of the massif there is only one snow-melt discharge peak.

Liard Plateau and Rocky Mountain Foothills

This is an area of 31,700 square kilometres much of which is covered by boreal forest in the northern part of the province. About 7000 square kilometres is occupied by the Liard Plateau in the Liard River basin. This is the southern termination of the Mackenzie Mountains geologic structure, with north-south trending sedimentary rock structures contrasting with the northwesterly trend of the Rocky Mountains. The average summit elevation is 1300 to 1500 metres and the plateau slopes gently eastwards. There are no hydrometric data for this region and discharge intensities can only be inferred from data for the Liard River between Lower Post and Fort Liard. About 7000 square kilometres of the Rocky Mountain Foothills region is in the Liard River basin and the remainder is in the Peace River basin. This region is underlain by strongly folded and faulted sedimentary rocks which become less strongly folded towards the east. Hydrometric data from three stations[14] indicate a mean discharge intensity of 0.014 c.m.s. per square kilometre (or about 440 millimetres mean annual runoff). Sometimes a May maximum discharge following breakup and a June-July snowmelt peak show up as two separate peaks in the discharge record, but over the long term only one major peak can be distinguished. It is likely that the discharge intensity quoted is somewhat low as the data for the Pine and Halfway rivers are influenced by the less humid Alberta Plateau region.

Rocky Mountains

Of the 91,000 square kilometres occupied by the Rocky Mountains physiographic region in British Columbia, 29,000 is in the Peace River basin, 27,000 in the Columbia River basin, 25,000 in the Liard River basin, and 10,000 in the Fraser River basin. There are four distinct ranges within the region known as the Border, Continental, Hart, and Muskwa ranges, and distinctions are based largely on geologic structure and physiography. The whole region is characterized by massive limestones, quartzites, and argillites which go to form massively bold peaks, best expressed in the Park Ranges of the Continental Ranges area.

The Park Ranges contain some of the most spectacular and heavily glaciated mountain ranges in North America. Flat to gently dipping beds of

14 Sikanni Chief River (10CB-1), 2070 sq. km., 1958–67; Halfway River near Farrell Creek (7FA-1), 9400 sq. km., 1961–7; Pine River at East Pine (7FB-1), 12050 sq. km., 1964–7.

quartzite or limestone have produced castellated peaks, subsequently modified by glacial oversteepening; large talus cones have developed postglacially. Hydrologically, the most significant factors are the steep slopes, the high available relief, and the continued presence of glaciers. Summit elevations decline both northwards and southwards from the Park Ranges, and the Hart Ranges in particular are considerably lower than the other ranges. Elevations increase again in the Muskwa Ranges, and the castellated limestone and quartzite peaks reappear around Mount Churchill (3200 metres) and Mount Lloyd George (3000 metres). Hydrometric data from nine stations[15] in this region indicate a mean discharge intensity of 0.031 c.m.s. per square kilometre (or about 980 millimetres mean annual runoff), ranging from 0.045 in the Fraser River basin to 0.019 in the Liard River basin. Stations typical of the Park Ranges and Muskwa Ranges show two prominent discharge peaks corresponding to snowmelt (June) and glacier melt (July-August) and a minor peak in the fall. In the Hart Ranges the glacier melt peak is absent in general, and in the Border Ranges to the south there is neither a fall rains peak nor a glacier melt peak.

Alberta Plateau

This is the second largest physiographic region in the province, with about 42,000 square kilometres in the Peace River basin and about 61,600 square kilometres in the Liard River basin. This plateau lies between about 800 and 1200 metres above sea level and is underlain by shales and sandstones which dip gently to the east forming plateaus and cuestas. All the hills are capped by a relatively smooth surface on which drainage is poorly organized. The Peace River valley was occupied by the pro-glacial Lake Peace, and in this area lake sediments as thick as 30 to 40 metres have been reported (Mathews 1955, 1963).

Hydrometric data from four stations[16] indicate a mean discharge in-

---

15 Toad River above Nonda Creek (10BE-4), 2570 sq. km., 1961–7; Kwadacha River near Ware (7EA-2), 2410 sq. km., 1960–7; Parsnip River below Misinchinka River (7EE-6), 5520 sq. km., 1966–7; McGregor River at Lower Canyon (8KB-3), 4765 sq. km., 1960–7; Moose River at Red Pass (8KA-8), 497 sq. km., 1955–67; Wood River near Donald (8NC-1), 922 sq. km., 1942–56 and 1965–7; Kootenay River at Canal Flats (8NF-2), 5390 sq. km., 1944–50 and 1963–7; Bull River near Wardner (8NG-2), 1500 sq. km., 1927–67; Flathead River at Flathead (8NP-1), 1165 sq. km., 1951–67.

16 Kiskatinaw River near Farmington (7FG-1), 3290 sq. km., 1962–4 and 1965–7; Blueberry River below Aitken Creek (7FC-3), 1750 sq. km., 1964–7; Beatton River near Fort St John (7FC-1), 16,100 sq. km., 1961–7; Fort Nelson River at Fort Nelson (10CC-1), 44,500 sq. km., 1960–7.

Table 3.3 Fraser River basin discharge: contributions from each physiographic region

Physiographic region	Discharge intensity (c.m.s./sq. km.)	Percentage of basin above Hope	Percentage of total basin	Discharge contribution to each sq. km. above Hope	Discharge contribution to each sq. km. of basin
Coastal Trough	0.021	—	1	—	0.00021
Coast Mountains	0.060	7	12	0.00420	0.00720
Cascade Mountains	0.045	2	2	0.00090	0.00090
Hazelton Mountains	0.020	1	1	0.00020	0.00020
Omineca Mountains	0.020	1	1	0.00020	0.00020
Interior Plateau	0.004	75	70	0.00300	0.00280
Columbia Mountains	0.035	9	8	0.00315	0.00280
Rocky Mountain Trench	0.008	0.5	0.5	0.00004	0.00004
Rocky Mountains	0.045	4.5	4.5	0.00202	0.00202

Mean discharge intensity 0.01371 0.01637
Mean discharge at Hope (1912–67) 2704 c.m.s.
Mean discharge for Fraser Basin (from table) 3814 c.m.s.
(−63 c.m.s. diverted to Kemano-Kitimat)

tensity of 0.005 c.m.s. per square kilometre (or about 160 millimetres mean annual runoff). The two discharge peaks of breakup and snowmelt are evident in most of the discharge records of this region.

MAJOR RIVER BASINS

A second way of dividing up the province is in terms of its constituent river basins. Six of the major river basins are now discussed.

The Fraser River Basin

The Fraser River basin has an area of about 233,000 square kilometres and an estimated mean annual discharge of 3814 cubic metres per second at its mouth. The mean annual precipitation for the whole basin is 991 millimetres (1931–60),[17] with a range from 192 millimetres at Ashcroft to 3560 millimetres at Coquitlam Lake. The mean discharge intensity for the Fraser basin is 0.016 cubic metres per second, which corresponds to about 500 millimetres of runoff per year (Table 3.3).

Figure 3.4 illustrates some of the discharge frequency characteristics of the Fraser River at two locations, one above Texas Creek and the other at Hope. At Texas Creek, south of the village of Lillooet, the area drained by the Fraser is 138,800 square kilometres and at Hope the comparable figure is 216,500. The most frequently occurring discharge is about 600 c.m.s. for the Fraser River at Texas Creek and about 800 c.m.s. at Hope, and these low discharges are recorded during the winter months of January, February, and March. The mean discharges, which are 1866 and 2723 c.m.s. respectively, are exceeded only 40 per cent of the year, and such high discharges occur from May to September, and sometimes in October. The late May–early June period corresponds to the snowmelt-induced highest discharges of the year; in July, August, and early September the glacial melt component is considerable and in late September and October the fall rains of the western half of the basin may cause above-average flows.

Two major floods have occurred in the recorded history of the Fraser River. The first was in 1894, when an estimated 17,000 c.m.s. discharge occurred, and the second was in 1948, when 15,180 c.m.s. was recorded at Hope on May 31st. Subsequently extensive engineering works have been completed in the lower Fraser Valley and two major right-bank trib-

---

17 In the succeeding paragraphs, mean annual basin precipitation was determined by planimetry from Figure 3.2. The precision of this statistic is low in, for example, the Stikine River basin, where only one long-term precipitation record exists.

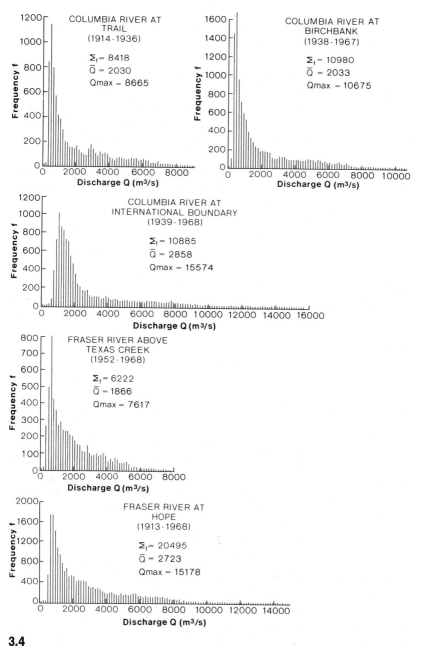

3.4
Discharge-Frequency Graphs for Columbia and Fraser Rivers

utaries of the Fraser, the Nechako and the Bridge, have been dammed. In the case of the Nechako River, its headwaters have actually been diverted through a hydropower tunnel to Kemano on the Pacific coast. These developments might have been expected to have reduced the flood hazard in the lower Fraser. In spite of these drainage changes, however, recent work has shown that during the period 1953–69 mean discharges recorded on the Fraser River have been markedly higher than during the period 1913–52 (Slaymaker 1972). Indeed, during the 1953–69 period, the mean daily discharge exceeded the long-term average in all years except 1953 and 1956 (Figure 3.5). Analysis of the precipitation data for the Fraser basin has not revealed any comparable trend, and it is therefore apparent that the mean discharge increase must be the result of one or more of five factors: (a) systematic errors in stream gauging, (b) land use changes such as deforestation, (c) progressive melting of glaciers, (d) precipitation increase at high levels where no rain gauges are located, (e) the presence of high-density snowfalls from Pacific storms which have a higher water equivalent than average.

The first alternative is unlikely because the gauging station at Hope is thought to be the most reliable in the Fraser River system, and the increase that has occurred since 1952 is independently recorded at those stations upstream from Hope. The second alternative is a possible aggravating factor, though it can scarcely account for as much as a 9 per cent increase in mean daily discharge over a 233,000 square kilometre basin. The possibility that glacier melt has caused the increase in mean daily discharge is difficult to confirm or reject. The Glacier Survey of Alberta (Campbell et al. 1969a) shows rates of ablation measured on the Saskatchewan Glacier which would produce mean discharge increases of 4 per cent over a 20-year period. The ice ablation data for British Columbia (Campbell et al. 1969b) are extremely variable, but all are considerably lower than those reported for the Saskatchewan Glacier, so it would be unjustifiable to ascribe more than a small percentage of the discharge increase to glacier melt. It seems that increase in precipitation (and particularly snowfall) in ungauged areas of the Fraser River basin must be a major factor causing the mean discharge increase. As there are no rain gauges above 1000 metres in the northern part of the Fraser Basin, this would seem to be a possible source of the additional runoff. The mechanism that would account for additional precipitation in this part of the province is a more northerly mean position of the Arctic front during recent years and consequently a more extensive influence of the Pacific air mass in the interior of British Columbia.

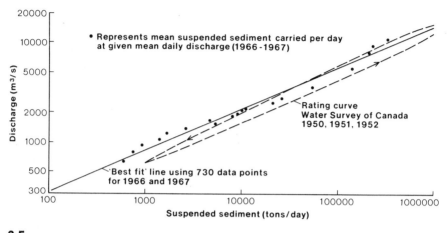

3.5
Mean Annual Discharge for the Fraser River at Hope (1913–68)

Sediment Movement in the Fraser River

Records of sediment movement in British Columbia's rivers are more elusive than discharge data, and any generalizations made from the comparatively few available data should be viewed with caution. The most reliable sediment movement data are collected on the Fraser River at Hope, and since 1966 the Sediment Survey of Canada has carried out routine sampling at this site. In addition, data are available for 1950–2 when the Water Survey of Canada collected water and sediment samples there. Figure 3.6 summarizes three alternative ways of presenting these data. First, and most correctly, is the envelope curve, which is derived by plotting separately those observations made during rising and falling stages. The graph shows a well-established phenomenon that the amount of sediment carried by a river during the rising stage is greater than during the falling stage, given comparable discharges. This is because the amount of sediment moved by a river is a function of the rate of supply of sediment to that river from banks and tributary slopes as well as a function of discharge. Secondly, and least precisely, is the plot of the average amount of sediment transported per day for every day when the mean discharge was within ±100 c.m.s. of given discharge values (see black dots on Figure 3.6). Thirdly, and most usefully, is the best-fit line plotted by the method of least squares to 730 data points, which then predicts an average sediment load per day for any given discharge.

A magnitude-frequency curve for the Fraser River at Hope, showing

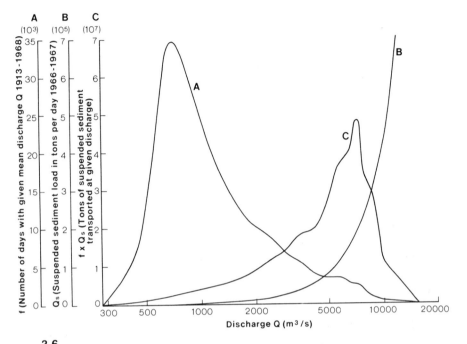

3.6
Suspended Sediment Rating Curves for the Fraser River at Hope
(1950–2 and 1966–7)

the discharge range within which most of the work of transporting sediment past Hope has been done during 1913–68, derives directly from Figures 3.5 and 3.6. The interesting observation which becomes apparent, and which has frequently been made in other environments, is that the highest discharge events of 11,000 c.m.s. and above have done substantially less work during the historical period of record than have discharges in the 7000 to 8000 c.m.s. range (Figure 3.7). Every year during the end of May and the beginning of June the Fraser flows in this discharge range, and so it can be said that the frequent flows are apparently more significan than the extreme flows in transporting sediment in the Fraser River.

The changes in sediment discharge over post-glacial time have been investigated in the Fraser basin by Church and Ryder (pers. comm.). Ryder (1971), in her studies of alluvial fans and other fluvial and lacustrine sediments in the Fraser and Columbia River basins, has documented up to 180 metres of post-glacial sands and gravels and possibly 200 metres of post-glacial lacustrine silt. The alluvial fan deposits are in

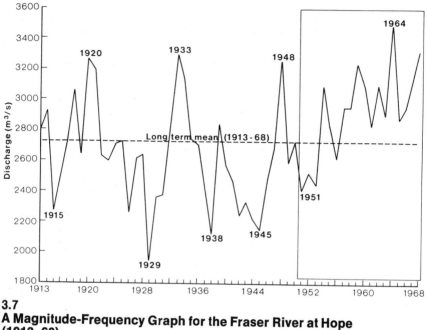

3.7
A Magnitude-Frequency Graph for the Fraser River at Hope (1913–68)

general superimposed on the sands and gravels, indicating that aggradation in the main valleys was effectively completed before fan building had ended. By dating the end of the period of fan building through the presence of Mazama ash one to two metres below the surface of the fans, Ryder has deduced that post-glacial sedimentation was concentrated in the period 10,000 to 6,000 years B.P. If sedimentation was proceeding continuously or semicontinuously during these 4000 years, then the average rate for the middle Fraser basin was of the order of 650 tons per year per square kilometre. This is, of course, a conservative figure (the present rate of sediment transport is about 130 tons per year per square kilometre above Hope),[18] and rates of aggradation must have been considerably higher over shorter time periods, because there are no dated horizons closer together than 1000 years or so; however, peak rates cannot be ascertained. It is sufficient to note that the alluvial valley-fills of south-central British Columbia suggest sedimentation rates at least an order of magnitude greater than those now recorded on the Fraser River at Hope.

18 This figure, derived from sediment load data, is of the same order of magnitude as that estimated by Mathews and Shepard (1962) with Fraser delta accumulation data.

Work in the Lillooet River basin near the village of Pemberton is demonstrating ways in which sediment discharge rates vary over time as a result of the economic development of a rural community. The area has an unusually high rate of sediment movement through its rivers, corresponding to about 290 tons per year per square kilometre, because of the large number of glaciers in its headwaters, the available relief of up to 2300 metres, the mean maximum valley-side slopes of 40–45° and the presence of highly erodible Quaternary volcanics. In 1946, the Water Development Branch of the Prairie Farm Rehabilitation Administration commenced a major reclamation programme in the Lillooet valley by introducing engineering works to train the river course, straightening and shortening it from headwaters to the delta. The increased velocity of the steepened river, combined with rapid changes in land use patterns of the area, has produced sediment movement rates up to four times as great as those recorded prior to 1946, or about 1160 tons per year per square kilometre. In this way, the 20-year average sediment movement rate in the Lillooet basin has been increased to an order of magnitude comparable with immediate post-glacial conditions in south-central British Columbia.

Any summary of sediment movement in the Fraser basin would be incomplete without reference to the dissolved load which is carried by the streams of the basin and which commonly determines the quality of the water for industrial and other purposes. In general, in the Fraser basin the quality of the surface waters is appropriate for industrial and other uses with little or no treatment to alter the mineral content because moderately soft water (low total hardness as calcium carbonate) is characteristic. It is therefore possible to make the generalization that in the Fraser basin it is the turbidity of the rivers rather than the quality of their waters which inhibits their use for industrial and domestic purposes. There is a general decrease in hardness of the Fraser waters towards the sea, primarily because the major source of calcareous rocks in the basin is the headwaters area in the Rocky Mountains. Right-bank tributaries of the Fraser bring softer waters from the Coast Mountains and dilute the calcalcareous content of the Fraser River waters progressively downstream.

The Columbia River Basin

The Columbia River basin has an area of 102,000 square kilometres in British Columbia and an estimated mean annual discharge deriving from this area of 2193 c.m.s. A left-bank tributary of the Columbia, the Kootenay River, rises in the Rocky Mountains, enters the United States, and drains a 15,500 square kilometre area of Montana and Idaho before join-

Table 3.4 Columbia River basin discharge: contributions from each physiographic region

Physiographic region	Discharge intensity (c.m.s./sq. km.)	Percentage of basin above Birchbank	Percentage of total basin in B.C.	Discharge contribution to each sq. km. above Birchbank	Discharge contribution to each sq. km. of basin in B.C.
Rocky Mountains	0.021	38	26	0.00798	0.00546
Rocky Mountain Trench	0.006	2	2	0.00012	0.00012
Columbia Mountains	0.028	60	55	—	0.00090
Interior Plateau	0.006	—	15	—	0.00030
Cascade Mountains	0.015	—	2	—	0.00030
Mean discharge intensity				0.02490	0.02218
Mean discharge at Trail (1913–37) and Birchbank (1937–67)				2019 c.m.s.	
Mean discharge for Columbia basin (from table)				2262 c.m.s.	

ing the Columbia River in British Columbia. Two right-bank tributaries, the Okanagan and Kettle rivers, flow into the state of Washington before joining the Columbia River, and the Similkameen River flows into Washington before joining the Okanagan River. 15,500 square kilometres of the Columbia basin in British Columbia are drained by the Similkameen, Okanagan, and Kettle rivers. The mean annual precipitation for the whole basin in British Columbia is 1161 millimetres (1931–60), with a recorded range from 258 millimetres at Keremeos to 1938 millimetres at Rogers Pass. The mean discharge intensity for the Columbia basin is 0.022 c.m.s. per square kilometre, which corresponds to about 690 millimetres of runoff per year (Table 3.4).

Discharge-frequency characteristics (Figure 3.4) and the time distribution of these discharges can only be understood in the context of (a) the influence of the Columbia River Treaty on the regulation of river flow and (b) the irrigation water requirements of the Okanagan valley. The Treaty dams, the Duncan, Arrow, and Mica, will all influence the flow of the Columbia River at Birchbank in such a way that the discharge-frequency curves shown will become a matter of historical record. Different flow characteristics will be reported when the new dams are in operation.

Sediment Movement in the Columbia River

Turbidity levels in the streams of the Columbia basin appear to be comparable to those in the Fraser basin from the two station records on the Kootenay River at Porthill and the Columbia River at Revelstoke which provide continuous records. For the Kootenay River at Porthill the rate of suspended sediment movement per square kilometre of its 35,500 square kilometre basin area is about 75 tons per year (1965–7); for the Columbia River at Revelstoke, with 26,000 square kilometres of basin area, the rate is about 170 tons per square kilometre per year (1966–7). The high percentage of glacier coverage of headwater basins, steep slopes, and erodible materials influence the rate of growth of the Incommapleux River delta at the head of the Upper Arrow Lake.

In addition to the turbidity of the waters of the Columbia basin, their comparative hardness relative to the waters of the Fraser inhibits their economic utilization. In particular, the waters of the Okanagan valley are comparatively heavily mineralized. One of the prime objectives of the Okanagan River Basin Study now in progress is to set down standards for the protection of headwater supply areas so that extensive lake eutrophication can be averted. In the main Columbia valley, water hardness results from the highly calcareous bed-rock over which the river flows in

Table 3.5 Peace River basin discharge: contributions from each physiographic region

Physiographic region	Discharge intensity (c.m.s./ sq. km.)	Percentage of basin above Taylor	Percentage of total basin	Discharge contribution to each sq. km. above Taylor	Discharge contribution to each sq. km. of basin
Alberta Plateau	0.004	14	32	0.00056	0.00128
Rocky Mountain Foothills	0.014	18	14	0.00252	0.00196
Rocky Mountains	0.025	27	22	0.00675	0.00550
Rocky Mountain Trench	0.008	2	1	0.00016	0.00008
Omineca Mountains	0.018	29	22	0.00522	0.00396
Cassiar Mountains	0.015	4	3	0.00060	0.00045
Interior Plateau	0.006	5	4	0.00030	0.00024
Stikine Plateau	0.011	1	1	0.00011	0.00011
Mean discharge intensity				0.01622	0.01358
Mean discharge at Taylor (1951–67)				1470 c.m.s.	
Mean discharge for Peace basin (from table)				1738 c.m.s.	

its upper reaches, but in the Okanagan and to a lesser extent the Kettle valleys, the heavy mineralization of the water is a result of the extensive use of local water for irrigation (Thomas 1953–4).

The Peace River Basin

The Peace River basin has an area of about 128,000 square kilometres and an estimated mean annual discharge of 1560 c.m.s. as it enters Alberta. The Peace River used to be formed by the junction at Finlay Forks of the Finlay and Parsnip rivers. This junction is now inundated below the waters of Williston Reservoir behind Bennett Dam, and many of the discharge-frequency characteristics of the Peace River discussed below have been changed by the construction of this major dam. The Finlay River rises on the Stikine Plateau and the Parsnip River rises in the western side of the Rocky Mountains. The Peace has cut through the Rocky Mountains and the Rocky Mountain Foothills, leaving the Foothills by means of the Peace River Canyon at Hudson Hope. It is west of this site that the Bennett Dam has been built.

The mean annual precipitation for the whole basin is 800 millimetres (1931–60), with a range from 425 millimetres at Taylor Flats to 2389 millimetres at Pine Pass. The mean discharge intensity for the Peace basin is 0.014 c.m.s. per square kilometre, which corresponds to about 440 millimetres of runoff per year (Table 3.5).

Figure 3.8 illustrates some of the discharge-frequency characteristics of the Peace River at two locations prior to the construction of the Bennett Dam. At Hudson Hope the area drained by the Peace is 72,000 square kilometres, and near Taylor the area is 99,000 square kilometres. The most frequently recorded discharges were about 300 c.m.s. at Hudson Hope and about 400 c.m.s. near Taylor, and these were typically recorded through the months of December to April. The mean discharge, which was 1083 and 1445 c.m.s. respectively, was exceeded less than 30 per cent of the year, and such high discharges occurred during May, June, and July. The period of high flows was considerably shorter than in the Columbia and Fraser basins and was confined to the snowmelt peak periods following ice breakup.

Considerable controversy has surrounded the Bennett Dam over the last year or two in that allegations have been made to the effect that the ecology of the Peace-Athabasca delta in Alberta has been transformed adversely by its construction. Of incontrovertible significance is the changed sediment discharge regime which the Peace River must develop downstream from the Bennett Dam. During 1965–7 the sediment transported by the Peace at Peace River, Alberta, averaged, for the 187,000

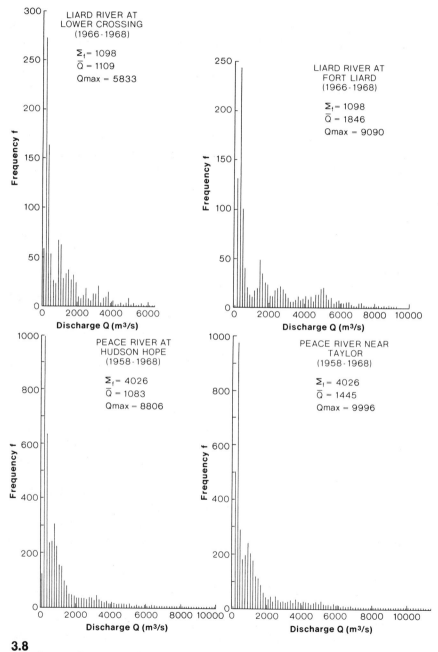

3.8
Discharge-Frequency Graphs for Liard and Peace Rivers

square kilometre basin, 250 tons per square kilometre per year. This is a higher rate than that recorded for either the Fraser or the Columbia, and the cutting off of a considerable portion of the sediment supply area upstream by the dam will initiate accelerated erosional activity by the Peace River downstream from the dam.

The Liard River Basin

The Liard River basin has an area of about 144,000 square kilometres in British Columbia and an estimated mean annual discharge of 1380 c.m.s. generated in the province. This is only a small part of the Liard basin, which rises in the Yukon and joins the Mackenzie River in the Northwest Territories. The mean annual precipitation for the whole basin is 663 millimetres (1931–60), with a range from 401 millimetres at Dease Lake to 719 millimetres at Cassiar. The mean discharge intensity for the Liard basin is 0.011 c.m.s. per square kilometre, which corresponds to about 350 millimetres of runoff per year (Table 3.6).

Figure 3.8 illustrates some of the discharge-frequency characteristics of the Liard River at two locations. At Lower Crossing the area drained by the Liard is 104,500 square kilometres, and at Fort Liard the area is 222,000 square kilometres. The most frequently recorded discharges are about 300 c.m.s. at Lower Crossing and about 450 c.m.s. at Fort Liard, and these are typically recorded during the same months as the low flows on the Peace. The mean discharges, which are 1109 and 1806 c.m.s., are exceeded about 30 and 35 per cent of the year respectively. Whereas at Lower Crossing these high flows occur typically during May, June, and July, at Fort Liard August is commonly also a high discharge month. This can probably be explained in terms of the lower gradient and higher base flow component of the Fort Nelson River, a major tributary of the Liard above Fort Liard.

Little is known about the sediment-transporting characteristics of the Liard River. Scattered data from a British Columbia Provincial Government Survey of the Liard River in 1961 give some first estimates of sediment loads. On one day in June 1961, a total suspended sediment load in the Muskwa River of 620,000 tons was estimated. This is equivalent to the highest daily load ever recorded for the Fraser River at Hope, which drains ten times the area of the Muskwa. Other single-day measurements were made on the Liard itself and on the Hyland, Coal, Smith, Toad, Racing, and Sikanni Chief rivers during the same survey, but it is difficult to make quantitative statements comparing these data with those for other British Columbia streams.

Table 3.6 Liard River basin discharge: contributions from each physiographic region

Physiographic region	Discharge intensity (c.m.s./ sq. km.)	Percentage of basin above Ft. Liard	Percentage of basin in B.C.	Discharge contribution to each sq. km. above Ft. Liard	Discharge contribution to each km. of basin
Stikine Plateau	0.011	6	2	0.00066	0.00022
Cassiar Mountains	0.015	15	20	0.00225	0.00300
Liard Plain	0.011	12	8	0.00132	0.00088
Rocky Mountain Trench	0.009	1	1	0.00009	0.00009
Liard Plateau	0.011	10	5	0.00110	0.00055
Rocky Mountains	0.019	16	17	0.00304	0.00323
Rocky Mountain Foothills	0.012	5	5	0.00060	0.00060
Alberta Plateau	0.005	35	43	0.00175	0.00210
Mean discharge intensity				0.01081	0.01067
Mean discharge at Fort Liard (1966–8)				1846 c.m.s.	
Mean discharge for Liard basin (from table)				1536 c.m.s.	

The Stikine River Basin

The Stikine River basin has an area of about 51,000 square kilometres in British Columbia and an estimated mean annual discharge of 1350 c.m.s. where it enters Alaska. The Stikine River rises on the Stikine Plateau and cuts through the Coast Mountains on its way to the Pacific Ocean. It has apparently maintained its course through the Coast Mountains by down-cutting more rapidly than the Pliocene orogeny could lift up the land mass. The estimated mean annual precipitation for the whole basin is 1180 millimetres (1931–60), with Telegraph Creek, recording 326 millimetres, as the only long-term station in the basin. The mean discharge intensity for the Stikine basin is 0.029 c.m.s. per square kilometre, which corresponds to about 910 millimetres of runoff per year (Table 3.7).

Figure 3.9 illustrates some of the discharge-frequency characteristics of the Stikine River at two locations. At Grand Canyon, the area drained by the Stikine is 18,900 square kilometres, and at Telegraph Creek it is 29,000 square kilometres. The most frequently occurring discharge is about 75 c.m.s. at Grand Canyon and about 100 c.m.s. at Telegraph Creek, and these low discharges are recorded during the winter months of December to April. The mean discharges, which are 291 and 373 c.m.s respectively, are exceeded about 35 per cent of the time, notably in May, June, July, and August. Unfortunately these records give an indication of the characteristics of the Stikine discharge only at points upstream before the influence of the Coast Mountains and fall rains is felt. It is clear that if data were available for the Stikine at the International Boundary, both a glacier melt peak and a fall rains peak would appear in addition to the simple snowmelt peak recorded above.

Recent investigations in the lower Stikine basin, notably in the Iskut River valley, have revealed further excellent hydroelectric power sites which may be developed soon. Planning is, however, hampered by the lack of long-term reliable yield data.

The Skeena River Basin

The Skeena River basin has an area of about 54,000 square kilometres and is contained entirely within British Columbia. The estimated mean annual discharge is about 1730 c.m.s., which is greater than that of either the Liard or the Peace with twice the drainage area. The mean annual precipitation for the whole basin is 1374 millimetres (1931–60), with a range from 431 millimetres at Telkwa to 2461 millimetres at Prince Rupert. The mean discharge intensity for the Skeena basin is 0.031 c.m.s. per square kilometre, which corresponds to about 980 millimetres of runoff per year (Table 3.8).

Table 3.7 Stikine River basin discharge: contributions from each physiographic region

Physiographic region	Discharge intensity (c.m.s./ sq. km.)	Percentage of basin above Telegraph Creek	Percentage of basin in B.C.	Discharge contribution to each sq. km. above Telegraph Creek	Discharge contribution to each sq. km. of basin
Stikine Plateau	0.011	65	51	0.00715	0.00561
Cassiar Mountains	0.015	19	13	0.00285	0.00195
Skeena Mountains	0.022	16	10	0.00352	0.00220
Coast Mountains	0.075	—	26	—	0.01950
Mean discharge intensity				0.01352	0.02926
Mean discharge at Telegraph Creek (1965–8)				368 c.m.s.	
Mean discharge for Stikine basin (from table)				1492 c.m.s.	

Table 3.8 Skeena River basin discharge: contributions from each physiographic region

Physiographic region	Discharge intensity (c.m.s./ sq. k.m.)	Percentage of basin above Usk	Percentage of total basin	Discharge contribution to each sq. km. above Usk	Discharge contribution to each sq. km. of basin
Skeena Mountains	0.022	46	30	0.01012	0.00660
Stikine Plateau	0.011	1	1	0.00011	0.00011
Omineca Mountains	0.018	7	5	0.00126	0.00090
Interior Plateau	0.008	20	19	0.00160	0.00152
Nass Basin	0.029	10	7	0.00290	0.00203
Hazelton Mountains	0.025	16	21	0.00400	0.00525
Coast Mountains	0.090	—	16	—	0.01440
Hecate Depression	0.066	—	1	—	0.00066
Mean discharge intensity				0.01999	0.03147
Mean discharge at Usk (1936–67)			903 c.m.s.		
Mean discharge for Skeena basin (from table)			1699 c.m.s.		

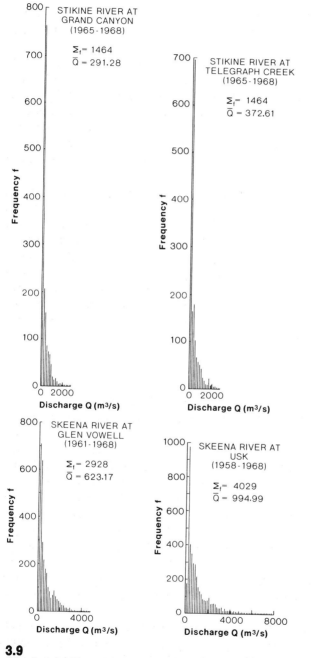

3.9
Discharge-Frequency Graphs for Skeena and Stikine Rivers

Figure 3.9 illustrates some of the discharge-frequency characteristics of the Skeena River at two locations. At Glen Vowell the area drained by the Skeena is 25,900 square kilometres, and at Usk it is 39,000 square kilometres. The most frequently occurring discharges are about 125 c.m.s. at Glen Vowell and about 175 c.m.s. at Usk, and these low discharges are recorded during January, February, March, and April. The mean discharges, which are 623 and 995 c.m.s. respectively, are exceeded about 40 per cent of the time, particularly in May, June, and July and parts of August, September, and October. Snowmelt, glacier melt, and fall rains all influence the high discharge characteristics of the Skeena basin.

The waters of the Skeena river system are chemically of high quality. The short average length of the streams and brief contact with the soil cause low pickup of soluble constituents from the soil, and so there are considerable quantities of very soft water. There is a decrease in the hardness of the Skeena water as it approaches the coast, as might be anticipated from the increasing dilution of the Bulkley River water, its major left-bank tributary. Turbidity during spring runoff is the only serious problem in the use of these waters, and the appearance of the main Skeena River during spring freshet suggests that even this problem may have been exaggerated.

CONCLUSIONS

These two contrasted methods of regional subdivision of British Columbia introduce the reader to two ways of reducing the extreme complexity of the physiography and hydrology of the province to a relatively small group of more homogeneous spatial entities. It is nevertheless clear that only in the southern part of the province, and specifically in the Fraser and Columbia River basins, are there adequate data on the climate and hydrology of both the morphological systems (physiographic regions) and the cascading systems (river basins) which have been described. Enough data do exist to describe the broad physiographic and hydrologic patterns of the province, the major features of the physiography and hydrology of the six river basins, and the physiographic details of the constituent physiographic regions. Some data are becoming available on the variations in hydrologic parameters over time, but this is still a matter for detailed local research.

In British Columbia it has been customary to consider ways in which engineering controls on the regional hydrology have beneficially influenced land use patterns, and as an example the diking programme in the lower Fraser Valley can be cited. It is becoming apparent (Jeffrey 1968; Slaymaker & Jeffrey 1969) that the influence of engineering works and of concomitant land use changes on the regional hydrology is inadequately understood. There appear to be significant changes in mean discharge, extreme discharges, timing of discharge events, sediment discharges, and water quality which represent major perturbations in our physical environment. These derive to a greater or lesser extent from regional land use changes concomitant with British Columbia's population growth. Until the detailed interrelationships between physiography, land use, and hydrologic response are better understood, costly mistakes may continue to be made by the planners of the future of the province.

ACKNOWLEDGMENTS

Acknowledgment is made to Mr J.H. Doughty-Davies, Senior Hydraulic Engineer with the British Columbia Water Resources Service, Victoria and to Dr J.L. Robinson, Department of Geography, University of British Columbia, for their critical reading of early drafts. The Canada Land Inventory gave permission for the reproduction of Figure 3.2 as modified from the *Agroclimatological Atlas of British Columbia*. Dr A.L. Farley, Department of Geography, University of British Columbia, gave permission for the reproduction of Figure 3.1 as modified from the *British Columbia Atlas of Resources*.

4 Economic Geography 1960-70

K.G. DENIKE and ROGER LEIGH

British Columbia has experienced extensive private investment in its resources, and the provincial landscape frequently illustrates the ephemeral nature of resource exploitation. Logged-over areas and abandoned mines are common, though among the urban population there is no great sensitivity to the role that resources play in the economy of the province and, indeed, a general lack of appreciation of the long-term benefits of large-scale resource-oriented projects.

A survey of the economic geography of British Columbia which sought only to elucidate the pattern of employment specialization would serve but to illustrate regional differences. An alternative approach is therefore followed in this chapter. The increasing interdependence of the provincial economy is emphasized; in this way it is possible to impart a picture of its basic coherence. By stressing interdependence, rather than merely accounting for regional differences, reasons emerge for the fact that British Columbia had, for example, the highest percentage population growth rate and the second highest personal income growth rate in Canada in the early 1960s (for 1961–5, see Economic Council of Canada 1965). An obvious difficulty with emphasizing connectedness is that the analysis becomes complex, and hence subject to a higher degree of personal interpretation than would arise with a more non-committal approach. Although unavoidable, this difficulty is partially alleviated by including a review of past, more intuitive, attempts at explaining changes in the provincial economy.

Since economic geography is taken to mean the analysis of structural and spatial characteristics in addition to their description, only limited attention is given here to an over-all view of the economy of British Columbia. This view is included in the first section of the chapter, where the province is described as having a rather simple resource-dependent economy (see Shearer 1968, chap. 1). Previous studies tended to elucidate simple descriptions, and these are reviewed in the following section. Having covered the background, the objectives of the present analysis and the methodology for evaluating the basic coherence of the economy are then outlined. In two later sections we discern the regional economic structure of the province and reflect on regional economic growth. Profiles of the economic maturity of each of the subregions are then indicated, in terms of stages of development, and finally the various bodies of evidence are brought together to form a model of the spatial interrelationship of the economy. It should be emphasized that the framework employed here is a dynamic one. Static comparisons are used solely as guide-posts, and rapid growth during the period of interest is stressed in terms of the fundamental coherence of the provincial economy.

Provincial Economy

The organization, markets, and competitive advantages of the forest and mining sectors play a critical role in the provincial economy. For over a century British Columbia has shown an almost classical pattern of economic development, related to the success of its export base industries. Over time, activities based on furs, gold, lumber, fish, and base metals have all attracted population and capital to the region and generated income for it. Although recent developments have increased the significance of the manufacturing and service sectors of the economy, they have not removed the dependence on industries which use the resources directly.

It is estimated that the forest and forest products industries directly or indirectly account for over one-half of the total income generated in the province (see Chapter 5). In the manufacturing sector, despite recent diversification, industries processing forest products are still the major export income-earners, and industries supplying the forest industry comprise much of the rest of local secondary industry. Hence, to a large extent the performance of the whole economy parallels that of the forest industry. In 1961 the state of foreign markets, and especially the U.S. market, for forest products was a major factor influencing the local economy. In 1961, the decline in the rate of home construction in the U.S. reverberated upon the B.C. economy. At times unemployment reached above 9 per cent, retail sales stagnated, and local home-building declined. Following 1961 the U.S. became a boom market for lumber because of its high rates of new family formation and household construction. With increased foreign demand, the B.C. economy expanded rapidly until the lack of mortgage money in the U.S. brought the boom market to an end in 1966. However, during the period 1961–6 the type of forest products which were exported changed. The products tended to have undergone greater processing prior to export than was the case before 1961. The changed character of the exports was instrumental in dampening the effects of the 1966 decline in

U.S. housing construction on the B.C. economy. The increased emphasis on exporting plywood, veneers, and wood pulp partially compensated for the effect of a severe decline in the availability of mortgage money, and consequently in the demand for construction lumber. What happened was that the diversification of exported products reduced the vulnerability of the province to variations in the price of lumber; broadening of the export base sustained the provincial economic boom into the late 1960s.

Whereas the forest industry was experiencing a historical transition from resource exploitation to resource processing between 1961 and 1966, the same was not true of the next largest exporting industry, mining. Much of the mining expansion in the late 1960s was tied to increased Japanese demand for relatively unprocessed products such as copper concentrates and coking coal. Although the growth of these mineral exports reduced the vulnerability of the economy to changes in demand for any one mineral product, it did little to alter the resource exploitation nature of the economy.

Thus the rapid economic expansion that British Columbia experienced in the 1960s (that saw the Gross Provincial Product increase by over 75 per cent to 7.5 billion dollars, and saw the population increase by 25 per cent to over 2 million) could be convincingly explained in terms of the export of resources: overseas industrial markets for B.C.'s raw and processed resources were buoyant, and B.C. had production and transfer cost advantages that enabled it to compete well in these markets against international rivals.

During the economic expansion phase of the 1960s, incomes rose faster than population in the province, an indication of the distinctive nature of the B.C. economy. Although the province is resource-based, it has an advanced economy. By comparison, most regions which depend on resource exploitation have 'primitive' economies, in which incomes remain stable and the population increases. More formally, an advanced economy is one that is highly connected. In British Columbia the basic exporting industries are closely linked to local secondary and tertiary industries. Increases in export sales result in extensive recycling of money and investment in the region, and finally in rising incomes for residents. Thus, although the province can fairly be described as having a simple economy (a resource-based and export-oriented economy) it also has an advanced, well-integrated economy with close connections between the resource sectors and other sectors; change in one has a great impact on the other.

Previous Studies

The gradual development of structural interconnections within the B.C.

apr. came into its own when the bottom fell out of the timber

economy has been commented on by several authors. Ingram, in 1958, described the growth of secondary industry in the province from the mid-19th century. He noted the growth of the resource-linked transport-equipment and forest-equipment industries in southwest B.C. as early as the 1890s, and also, in the same period, the development of small-scale industries to serve local consumer markets in the nationally isolated Vancouver area. He pointed out that industrialization was interrupted by the 1912 'bust' and the depression after World War I (e.g. projected steel mills and port facilities did not materialize), but that industrialization picked up again during and after World War II. The war created resources locally in the form of skilled labour and industrial suppliers and services; the postwar boom encouraged a widening of the range of local industries processing natural resources (e.g. more pulp mills and plywood plants, oil refineries, wineries) and supplying local resource industries (e.g. rope and logging equipment firms, steel pipe mills, chemical and fertilizer plants). Because these industrial developments were delayed by depression and war, recent changes seem all the more spectacular. The chief message in Ingram's account is of diversification of the industrial sector of the provincial economy through the taking up locally of forward linkages, in the form of local demand for resources, and backward linkages, through the growth of local industries to service the resource sector. Spatially much of this industrial development was concentrated in the Vancouver area throughout the period.

A similar message is contained in an article by Shearer (1968, chap. 1). He documents a shift in provincial employment ratios from the 1920s to the 1960s (Table 4.1). He interprets the employment changes in terms of the economic growth of a resource economy that is marked by increasing labour productivity in the primary sector. Further, the shifts in employment ratios are used to illustrate the development of more labour-intensive secondary and tertiary industries to supply and service both the resource sector and the increasingly wealthy urban population. Interestingly, Shearer explicitly distinguishes the evolution of the B.C. economy from that of an economy which changes from being initially resource-based to a later dependence largely on local demand for goods and services.[1] Thus he acknowledges increasing provincial diversification, but notes: 'Throughout all this diversity there is a common denominator; direct or indirect dependence on the extraction of natural resources – there is no evidence of

---

[1] For example, the fact that the resource sector is becoming more complex in its organization and administration is a major factor behind growth in the tertiary sector; this is different from a Clark-type interpretation of the shifts in the labour composition of the economy.

Table 4.1   Changing distribution of the labour force (from Shearer 1968)

	Percentage employment	
	1921	1961
Agriculture	16	4
Forestry	6	4
Fishing	2	1
Mining	5	1
Resource processing	9	12
Other manufacturing	7	8
Construction	7	6
Services	44	61
Not stated	5	3
	100	100

the secondary manufacturing replacing resource based activities in the economic base of the province.'

McGovern (1961), in his detailed study of industrial activity in the Lower Mainland area, also confirms these broad conclusions. He identified, by a survey of industrial plants, the metropolitan enterprises that sold most of their products outside British Columbia (these included sawmills, and plywood, veneer, fish, machinery, and fruit and vegetable plants) and also the enterprises which served the local market (including metal, transport equipment, chemical and petroleum firms serving industrial markets, and food, paper, and textile firms serving consumer markets). Although in the Lower Mainland the transition from a resource frontier to an urbanized, diversified, and interlinked industrial area is further advanced than elsewhere in the province, the dependence on the resource-processing functions was still detected.

The structural interconnections within the provincial economy also have spatial dimensions. Various regions of the province specialize in resource-related or population-related functions. These regions are interconnected and interdependent. The patterns of regional specialization and development implicit in the territorial arrangement of the provincial economy have also been sketched by some authors.

In the previously cited paper, Shearer (1968, p. 6) suggested a high-level generalizaion, a contrast between 'the city' (metropolitan Vancouver and Victoria) and the 'hinterland' (rest of the province). The latter was seen as the locus of space-using resource activities (agriculture and forestry), localized resource extraction (mining), and low-order service functions. The former was seen as the locus of break of bulk, external enonomy and market-oriented processing and manufacturing functions, of centres for the co-ordination and control of resource activities, and of high-order services.

This two-region model of the province, however, overestimates the role of Victoria (see Lycan and Forrester 1970, p. 94) and ignores the variation among the regions of the 'resource hinterland.' A better impression of the spatial interconnections of the province is given in the geohistorical account of Robinson and Hardwick (1968). Their theme is the increasing regional interactions that accompanied the growth of the provincial economy. On a hundred-year time scale they describe the early period of the economy (pre-1914) as one of 'speculation and exploitation.' During this period regions of the province were functionally isolated and experienced relatively independent economic development related to local resource development. Such resource exploitation was often impermanent and did not lead to the growth of large settlements in the regions. Following this period was a time of 'functional integration' (1914–46). Beginning with the coastal region, parts of the province became increasingly interconnected. For example, the coastal region supported a pattern of forestry activity where timber was taken from upcoast sites and transported to processing and shipping centres in the Georgia Strait region (see Chapter 5). A group of large, permanent settlements was established among which Metropolitan Vancouver was the key manufacturing and port centre. The most recent period (post-1946) saw the extension of metropolitan influences into the interior by the development of a co-ordinated network of roads, railways, and administrative services. In this stage of 'metropolitan dominance and integration,' urban centres have grown rapidly and have begun to specialize in some functions and to duplicate others. For example, the forest industry became dominated by large firms with head offices in Vancouver while processing and manufacturing began to be duplicated in centres such as Kamloops and Prince George.

Present Objectives

As can be seen from the preceding review, most previous studies offered a rather stylized view of the complex B.C. economy, and only roughly delineated the region. The question of geographical distribution in particular needs to be raised. The object of the rest of this chapter is to respond to this question, and thereby to offer both a broader and a more detailed discussion of the spatial organization of the provincial economy than has yet been provided. The essential difference between this and previous studies is the reliance here on statistical analysis of employment data, regional growth indices, and investment data. The analysis complements, rather than contradicts, the rather simple view of the province advanced in previous studies. Essentially our more detailed analysis aims to highlight the territorial dimensions of the interconnections of the provincial economy.

Regional Economic Structure

Since the object is to explain the regional patterns of economic development, the basic dimensions and spatial distribution of economic activities in the province are first described. The regions used in the analysis are modified major census divisions of 1961. The ten major regions (see Figure 4.1) are enlarged to twelve by treating Metropolitan Vancouver and Metropolitan Victoria as separate regions and the residual areas of census division 4 (southwestern B.C.) and 5 (Vancouver Island) as separate areas. These twelve regions are reasonably homogeneous economic units, though doubtless more complex patterns of economic specialization would be revealed by analysis of data at a finer areal scale (e.g. by paying more attention to interior urban regions).

The economic structure of the regions is considered in terms of ten major employment categories (agriculture; forestry; fishing, etc.; mining; manufacturing; construction; wholesale trade; retail trade; business and financial services; transport and utilities), using data from the 1961 Census. These data are then factor-analysed to elicit the similarities and differences in the spatial distribution of economic activity. The dominant component that emerges from the analysis is one which can best be described as an 'urban-service' component. The extent to which the 'urban-service' factor is present in an individual region depends on the importance of service employment and trade employment to the local economy. These activities vary together in relative importance over the province, being simultaneously important in more urbanized subregions. Two components of lesser importance are present and characterize distinctive resource-based activities. One indexes agriculture, and the other indexes mining. The appearance of two resource factors indicates the importance of these activities (each of which has a distinctive distribution among the subregions), and also helps to differentiate the hinterland subregions from one another. It is important to note that forestry does not show up as a distinctive component within the province, reflecting its widespread importance in all regions, i.e. the absence of any really distinctive distribution among the regions. However, as expected, there was a negative relationship between the urban-service component and employment in forestry in the most urbanized regions. This negative relationship also allows one to identify the hinterland regions which are most directly dependent on forestry.

Considerable regional variety exists within the province, within the framework of the basically simple aggregate provincial economy. Metropolitan Vancouver and Victoria have a high degree of urban services, indicating their role in the provincial economy; they are not centres of resource extraction, but rather of trade, co-ordination, and control (see Chapter 6). There is a superficial similarity of functions between these urban regions. The relationship of the regions to other parts of the province can be inferred: they articulate the provincial economy and service hinterland firms and households.

The Peace River (10), Okanagan (3), and Fraser Valley (4) all have dominant agricultural economies and less significant service roles, but forestry is important in each of these regions. Although agriculture is a specialization of all these regions, the nature of it differs from region to region. For example, the Fraser Valley supplies dairy products to the nearby urban markets, while the Okanagan produces fruit for provincial consumption as well for export (in fresh or processed form). In the Peace River region mining is also important; gas and oil are extracted and sent by pipeline to urban markets in the interior and southwestern regions of the province.

The East and West Kootenay areas are very similar; both emphasize mining and some service functions but not agriculture. Relative isolation allows local services to develop in these areas. Mineral resources (coal and base metals) are exported overseas via the port of Vancouver, the base metals having first been processed in the smelter at Trail.

Other subregions tend to have less distinctive economic profiles and hence cannot be so readily differentiated. However, there is an apparent similarity between the rather remote and sparsely populated regions of the Lower Coast (7), Vancouver Island (5), and Northwest Coast (9), for which there is no indication that agriculture or mining plays a significant role in the local economies. Forestry is virtually the sole resource base, and these subregions in fact include the major areas that supply logs to processing centres in southwestern parts of the province.

Table 4.2 summarizes the results of the factor analysis, and groups the regions into 'homogeneous' economic areas. The result is a more complex version of the city-hinterland model. The metropolitan regions are alike in being centres of service activity with no local resource-exploiting functions. Other subregions are essentially dependent on primary activity; forestry is characteristic of all regions, and the regions are differentiated from one another by the resource functions that accompany forestry (agriculture or mining) and by the importance of service functions locally.

Table 4.2   Economic specializations and similarities of regions, based on component scores (1961 data)

| | Urban-service component | Resource component | |
		Agriculture	Mining
Urban-service regions			
Metropolitan Vancouver	1.39	−0.14	−1.14
Metropolitan Victoria	2.13	−1.08	−0.23
Forest-mining regions			
East Kootenays (1)	+0.06	−0.01	2.54
West Kootenays (2)	+0.11	−0.35	+0.55
Forest-agriculture regions			
Okanagan (3)	−0.05	1.45	−1.22
Fraser Valley (4)	−0.46	1.08	−0.24
North-Central Interior (8)	−0.39	+0.05	−0.26
Kamloops–Thompson (6)	−0.15	+0.33	+0.21
Forest-based regions			
Vancouver Island (5)	−0.42	−0.70	−0.37
Lower Coast (7)	−1.90	−0.92	−0.76
Northwest Coast (9)	−0.54	−1.41	+0.24
Agriculture and mining region			
Peace (10)	+0.21	1.73	+0.67

Regional Economic Growth

From regional economic structure we turn to regional economic growth. The dimensions and patterns of economic growth of each of the subareas can be identified by growth indicators. The provincial economy grew rapidly during the decade of the sixties; some key indices are: population growth (25%, 1961–9), personal income (90%), total employment (40%), and manufacturing employment (56%). All the subregions also showed growth in these indices, but rates of growth varied widely among them. The greatest absolute growth in all indicators was shown by the already large metropolitan areas, but the greatest relative growth (in percentage change) was shown in the Peace and North-Central Interior region (10 and 8). Slower relative changes were shown by the southeastern region and the west coast.

The four growth indicators were summarized in terms of two basic dimensions of growth through principal components analysis. A general growth dimension was indicated by combining population, income, and employment variables; the second dimension indicated the significance of manufacturing. In other words, the first three variables were spatially indistinguishable, but this major pattern of growth was not associated with growth in manufacturing, which had its own distribution pattern. The separation of manufacturing from the general growth dimension illustrates that economic growth in the province was independent of growth in the manufacturing sector. This supports Shearer's statement that economic growth is not directly related to industrial expansion in B.C. The notion is apparently valid at the regional scale as well as the aggregate provincial level. Other factors must be responsible for economic growth in the various regions. Some probable factors are government investment, resource development, and urbanization, as will be discussed later.

In Table 4.3, regions are grouped according to the growth they experienced in the sixties. Since these groupings indicate changes, they are not necessarily compatible with the more static grouping of regions by economic specialization shown in Table 4.2.

The spatial distribution of economic growth is shown by the relationship of regions to the true dimensions of growth. The greatest growth was in the northern regions (Peace, North-Central Interior, and Northwest Coast), the urbanized southwest regions show slow or average growth

Table 4.3   Regional growth patterns, based on component scores (1961–9 data)

		General component	Manufacturing component
Rapid general and rapid manufacturing growth regions			
North-Central Interior	(8)	1.60	+0.71
Northwest Coast	(9)	1.37	+0.15
Rapid general and slow manufacturing growth regions			
Kamloops-Thompson	(6)	0.30	−0.29
Peace River	(10)	1.59	−1.06
Slow general and rapid manufacturing growth regions			
Metropolitan Vancouver		−0.43	+0.38
Fraser Valley	(4)	−0.70	1.41
Vancouver Island	(5)	−0.29	2.14
Stable or slow general and slow manufacturing growth regions			
East Kootenays	(1)	−1.23	−0.51
West Kootenays	(2)	−0.66	−0.94
Lower Coast	(7)	−0.91	−0.47
Victoria		−0.66	−0.83
Okanagan	(3)	+0.03	−0.68

rates, and the southeast the very lowest rates: the latter (the Kootenays) are in fact among the lowest-income areas of the province, with considerable population outmigration. The south-central region (Okanagan) has relative stability despite the labelling as a 'depressed' region given by a Federal government department.

The general pattern of expansion apparent from the analysis is essentially one of selective decentralization of population and economic activity to interior regions. This is a reflection of the very rapid percentage growth rates of northern and central areas compared to coastal urban centres, though the latter still retain their majority of the provincial population. Behind this interior growth and decentralization lies government investment in road, rail, and power facilities in the northern region, designed to permit resource development by large corporations. In the northwest and Peace regions the infrastructure is just being established. In the north-central region (region 8) close utilization of the forest resource, plus mineral extraction, is well advanced and resource-based settlements, in which resource-linked industries are developing, are in evidence (e.g. Prince George). Availability of Federal government mortgages encourages the growth of new towns in such regions and encourages population migration into hitherto remote districts.

This decentralization of population and economic activity is another unusual feature of the B.C. economy. In some other resource regions (e.g. the Prairies) centralization of population and activities into urbanized areas is the pattern (see Barr 1972). In B.C. local resources have sufficient capacity to sustain linked activities at greater intensities of exploitation than in other resource regions. In addition public development policies play a part in accelerating hinterland growth.

Manufacturing growth tends to distinguish the metropolitan regions, especially Metropolitan Vancouver, from the remainder of the province. Processing industries persist and grow there because of the ease of transporting resources to urban processing centres via coastal waterways and by extensions of the railway system. Metropolitan areas are also the natural location for industries oriented towards external economies and markets because of access to service and population. For example, Eastern manufacturers considering branch plant locations in B.C. rarely look beyond Metro Vancouver as a potential site for their operations (Employers Council of B.C. 1969). Other areas having high rates of manufacturing growth are the Lower Mainland (decentralization from Metropolitan Vancouver) and the North-Central Interior (development of resource-processing and local consumer industries). However, manufacturing growth is slow in most other areas; the real pattern is one of centralization of manufacturing into urban or urbanizing regions, while the population is decentralizing into interior and northern areas. (Table 4.3).

The north-central region experienced both high general growth and high manufacturing growth. Industrialization, as well as primary resource development, underlies the spectacular economic growth of this region. Indeed, the range of linked industries and consumer-oriented industries in the central city of Prince George is now sufficient to consider it as a 'growth pole'; this urban area has qualities of self-sustaining growth, deriving from the labour, service, and market advantages it offers. In this integrated region economic growth does not appear to depend so completely on external market forces (although they are significant for the lumber and pulp markets) since local industrial expansion and innovation should propel future growth.

Stages of Development
Another aspect of the spatial structure of the province concerns the roles that the various regions play in the provincial economy, and the level or stage of development attained by these regions. A region is considered to be at an elementary stage of development if it is dominated by resource-exploitative activities, and typified by small size of settlements supported by these activities. At higher stages, regions develop a range of linked industries upon the local resource base (further processing of resources, or the supply of materials and services to resource industries) as well as consumer-oriented industries of increasing scale. In the most complex regions, settlement includes large permanent centres that are capable of attracting or innovating new industries, and that stimulate new markets for local resources (e.g. agriculture, construction materials, energy). The dynamic of growth is then in large part within the cities of the region, rather than outside them in the markets for its exportable primary products, as is the case for less-developed regions. Developed regions are urban-focused and interdependent nodal regions; less-developed regions are homogeneous regions supporting loosely articulated small settlements (see Lithwick 1968).

The B.C. economy in aggregate is making a transition from an underdeveloped to an interconnected economy, some regions being affected more than others in the process. In geographical cross-section the province consists of interrelated regions at various stages of the sequence. Evidence to describe the regions in these terms comes from the record of investment compiled by the provincial government. For the decade of the 1960s, information was collected on the nature and scale of new investment and expansion in the twelve regions, in the primary and secondary industrial sectors, and in the areas of storage, transport, and power facilities (*Industrial Expansion in B.C.* 1960–9). The rates of investment per region were related by means of covariance analysis to selected socioeconomic indices. If a distinct relationship existed between the level of capital investment and the level of income in a region over a period of years, it was inferred that a region was at an elementary stage of development. At this stage investment shows up in the region as wages, and there are no local multiplier effects in population and retail sales. The building of dams in a remote, newly developing area, using migrant labour, is a typical example. With the transition to a more mature stage, urban centres provide certain services locally. Investment is then likely related most strongly to retail sales, as there is a propensity to spend locally. At high levels of sophistication, investment is related to manufacturing employment through greater industrial self-sufficiency as more linkages are created among industries and more market thresholds passed. At the highest level, investment is reflected in population growth.

The high degree of integration of British Columbia is confirmed by the very strong relationship between capital investment and population growth during the 1960s. To a large extent then, there is support for Robinson and Hardwick's view about the growing interrelationship of the provincial economy.

At the subregional level, Metropolitan Vancouver, as expected, records a strong relationship between investment and population, as is typical of highly developed subregions. As previously stated, this is a centre of head-office activity, local and extra-local private and public service functions, a wide range of industries (including most of the province's non-resource-based industries), as well as the transport facilities that articulate the entire provincial economy. It is a region of self-sustaining growth offering amenities not present in other cities in the province (see Chapter 6). Metropolitan Victoria does not show a significant relationship between investment and population. Victoria is probably not as functionally integrated, internally or with the rest of the province, as has been assumed. Additional support for this observation comes from Lycan and Forrester's analysis (1970, p. 94) of Victoria's telephone connections with other B.C. towns.

Regions at elementary stages of development are the Lower Coast (7) and the Northwest (9). They are rather sparsely populated areas at early stages of resource exploitation (e.g. export of logs for processing elsewhere). Less expected is the implication that the Okanagan region (3) is also at an early stage of development. Well-established agriculture, three medium-sized towns, and recent industrialization helped by Federal tax abatements characterize this valley. Perhaps proximity to the more attractive sites of Vancouver frustrates efforts to attract linked industry and consumer industries to the region.

Characteristic of a less primitive economy is the subregion of Vancouver Island, where investment is related most closely to retail sales. New towns such as Gold River have been established to process logs, and Port Alberni, for example, is a highly integrated forest-based industrial settlement. However, local demand is not yet sufficient to attract additional industries and services, although Nanaimo has rather intense business connections with centres in southwestern B.C. and could be considered a potential 'growth pole.'

Regions at an intermediate level of development (investment related to manufacturing employment) include the North-Central Interior (8). This region has had spectacular growth; several new pulp mills and related industries were established near Prince George after 1965. These have propelled the region to a high level of development. As Prince George attracts additional industries to supply the resource sector and develops industries to meet local consumer demands, its capacity for self-sustaining growth will be enhanced. In contrast to this subregion is the rather depressed Kootenay (1 and 2) area, where investment has been negatively related to manufacturing. Such a negative relationship indicates an increased importance of resource exploitation and the relative decline of the traditional industrial base of metal refining and log processing. Recent investment there has been in coal mining, the resource being shipped with minimal treatment directly to Japan.

Synthesis

Comparing the results of the preceding analyses, it is apparent that there are not always consistent relationships among the regions in terms of regional economic specializations, rates of growth, and levels of development. For example, the Okanagan (3) and Fraser Valley (4) had similar specializations but different growth experiences; the Kootenays (2) and Lower Coast (7) had different relations to investment, but grew at similar rates. An implication is that economic growth did not depend entirely on the initial economic speciality of a region in this period (it could also be related to public investment, or to decentralization of activities from adjacent regions, for example) and that rapid growth could be enjoyed by regions at different stages of development (i.e. regions could converge or overtake one another) since growth could depend on direct investment or on induced local changes.

However, despite these complexities, the results may be synthesized by taking a spatial viewpoint. The regions may be grouped together in an 'economic-geographic model,' which is a summary of the regional structure and development of the B.C. economy during the 1960s. The model is a variation on the 'heartland-hinterland' theme.

A small group of regions in the southwest constitutes the provincial urban heartland; the rest of the province is the resource hinterland. However, the internal variety of the heartland is recognized and, most important, the hinterland is divided into three broad *sectors,* which apparently differ from one another on the basis of the data analysed. Figure 4.1 illustrates the model.

The provincial *heartland* consists of the metropolitan areas of Vancouver and Victoria, plus the adjacent Lower Mainland region. The former urban centres have a similarity of economic specialization in their emphasis on co-ordinating and controlling service functions, and an absence of primary functions. The Lower Mainland region is included in the heartland because its agricultural specialization is strongly related to and dependent on these urban markets, and because it is increasingly the locus of manufacturing firms decentralizing from Metropolitan Vancouver. All parts of the heartland showed steady growth rates, and local advantages mean growth is assured in this zone.

The rest of the province make up the *hinterland.* Important contrasts within the hinterland are made clear by recognizing three broad sectoral groupings of regions as depicted in Figure 4.1. The first sector is the 'coastal' sector including Vancouver Island (5), the Lower Coast (7), and the Northwest Coast (9). The regions in this sector have a similarity in economic base, since specialization in forest activities is generally *not* supplemented by other resource activities. Possibly because of this narrowness of economic base, the coastal area has a slow economic growth experience. Public investment has been at a low level and has not been a compensating source of growth. However, manufacturing employment grew rapidly on Vancouver Island, and this region also showed a higher degree of internal interdependence than other parts of the sector. An announced provincial government policy of reserving Vancouver Island as an 'industry-free' zone may inhibit the move to a more advanced local economy.

The second sector, the 'northern central' or 'Interior,' has as its axis the British Columbia Railway (formerly the Pacific Great Eastern) and a focal point at Prince George; it includes the Kamloops-Thompson (6), North-Central Interior (8), and Peace (10). This is the most dynamic sector of the hinterland with a varied economic base. Agriculture supplements forestry there, and mining is important in the northern districts.

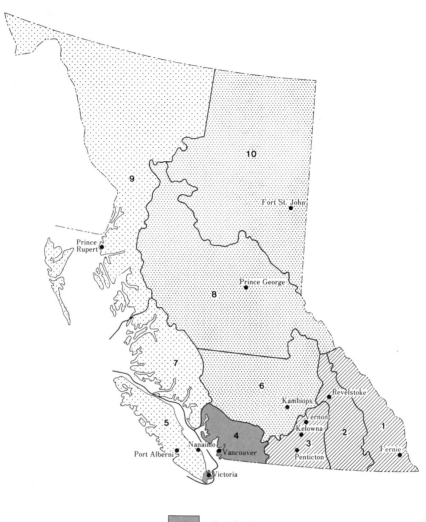

Prince Rupert

Fort St. John

10

9

Prince George

8

Revelstoke

7

6

Kamloops

Vernon

Kelowna

5

4

Nanaimo

Port Alberni

Vancouver

Penticton

Victoria

3

2

1

Fernie

Heartland

Hinterland:

Coastal sector

Interior sector

Southeast sector

Numbered regions are major census districts

4.1
An Economic-Geographic Model of British Columbia

Public investment and intense resource development give all parts a high rate of economic growth. Areas within the sector are at different stages of development, but the general impression is that the region is moving from resource exploitation through the development of linked industries to urban-supported growth. Economic development is most advanced in the Prince George region, where growth in manufacturing employment is also rapid. The influence of this subregion could eventually extend to the coast, linking the northwest region to this sector as new interdependencies develop. For example, enlarging the port of Prince Rupert could be instrumental in linking the coast to the interior.

The third sector, the 'south and southeastern' sector, is united by a varied resource base (agriculture and mining in addition to forestry) but also by slow rates of economic growth and the absence of evidence of tendencies to higher stages of development. Agriculture is more vulnerable to competition there than in the north-central region; the forest economy has been slower to move to more intensive levels of exploitation. The case of the mining industry is symptomatic of the problem in this sector. Although established early, it has not continued to attract resource-using industries. Since no urban centre is emerging as a potential growth pole, the forces capable of generating local growth have nothing around which to coalesce. Instead, urban facilities are dispersed among the small Okanagan and Kootenay cities. This is the most stagnant sector of the provincial hinterland. Incentive programmes have successfully lured manufacturing plants to some sections of the region, but consolidation of services into a leading centre is needed.

All these hinterland sectors are in different senses tributary to the heartland, and are controlled by or are dependent on certain heartland facilities. The dependence of the coastal sector is traditional and based on the supply of resources for heartland processing. The southeastern sector has more recently been integrated into the metropolitan sphere, as isolation has been broken down by improved transport. The subordination of the northern sector may be temporary, however, until Prince George supplements its range of functions and enlarges its sphere of influence. Provincial government policy has been of great significance in promoting the growth of the north-central sector, and encouraging the decentralization of population and activity into it.

Conclusion

It has been shown that although British Columbia's economy is based on resource exploitation, it is advanced. Hence economic growth in the 1960s was associated with rising incomes. Even in the peripheral areas of the province (such as the Peace), where the local economies are relatively primitive, the capital-intensive nature of the resource-based industries has generated rising incomes.

Most explanations of the provincial economy have stressed the continuing dependence on resource exploitation. This dependence has been largely confirmed by this analysis, but we have stressed also the essential interconnectedness of the economy. However, it would be dangerous to infer that the development of Metropolitan Vancouver directly reflects only increased resource activity. It would be more reasonable to suggest, on the basis of the analysis of investment data, that the viability of this subregion is increasingly the product of population increases. That these increases have not been larger is attributable in large part to the attraction of the resource hinterland to population and capital.

5 The Forest Resource

A.L. FARLEY[1]

It has been widely proclaimed that fifty cents out of every dollar spent in British Columbia is generated by the forest industry. The validity of this announcement is hard to deny. As a source of employment and as a generator of net production value, the primary and secondary phases of forest utilization far exceed their counterparts in other resource-based industries of the province.

Comparing the primary or extractive phases of industry, for example, the net value of logging production in 1960 approached $200 million, which was double the net value contributed by mining, over twice that of agriculture, and seven times the value of fishing. Similarly in manufacturing, the net value of production from all forest-based industries in 1960 was nearly $450 million, which was roughly half the total value of all manufacturing and about one-quarter of the net value of all commodity-producing industries. Available statistics for 1970 indicate that comparable relationships apply, clearly setting forestry as the keystone of the provincial economy.[2]

Forestry's share of the provincial labour force is also dominant, having been a close second to agriculture among the extractive industries in 1960, and having accounted for nearly half of the 113,000 total labour force in manufacturing industries. Although there has been spectacular growth in the province's mining and construction industries within the past decade, rapid expansion has also occurred in forest utilization. Recent statistics confirm forestry's pre-eminent share of the provincial labour force engaged in manufacturing, and its position second only to agriculture as an employer of labour in the primary sector.

1 The author is indebted to members of the Economics and Statistics Branch, Department of Industrial Development, Trade and Commerce, Victoria, B.C. for help in reconciling divergent data on the net production value and labour force, and for a critical reading of portions of the manuscript.
2 In official statistics since 1965, 'net annual value' for the primary phase of forestry has been replaced by 'value added,' which excludes stumpage and royalty.

Regionally, the relative importance of forest-based industries as producers of income and employment varies somewhat, but even in the regions of greatest industrial diversity and in those few where agriculture or mining are dominant, forestry is a very significant contributor. On a national scale, the British Columbia forest-based industries are also prominent. About 70 per cent of the sawn lumber produced in Canada, most of the plywood, and over one-quarter of the national production of chemical pulp comes from British Columbia forests. That the western province should contribute so large a share is not surprising if one considers the comparative resource endowment. In area, B.C.'s forested land comprises less than one-fifth of the national total, but it supports over half of Canada's remaining saw timber volume. Further, the species composition of the forests is such as to encourage their use for lumber, plywood, and strength pulp. In these respects, B.C.'s position nationally is not unlike that which Oregon, Washington, and Idaho hold in the comparable pattern of the United States. In fact there are many broad similarities between British Columbia and the adjacent Northwest States in terms of forest resource endowment and the nature and relative importance of industry based upon it. Available statistics do not permit detailed comparison, but they indicate that British Columbia has about twice the forested area and about one-third more timber volume than the combined states of Washington, Oregon, and Idaho.[3]

NATURE AND DISTRIBUTION OF THE RESOURCE

Forests in British Columbia are dominantly coniferous. The *Forest Inventory Statistics* for 1967 reports that, of a total mature forest volume of nearly 270 billion cubic feet, broad-leaved species make up less than 7½ billion. Table 5.1 makes it clear that, although the remaining volumes of spruce and hemlock are large, Douglas fir, the most desirable species for lumber and plywood, now accounts for less than 20 billion cubic feet of the mature wood volume.

In British Columbia the complex interplay of climatic controls is such as to produce climatic diversity greater than in any other part of Canada. Exemplifying the extremes, some stations on the exposed west coast have recorded annual totals well in excess of 150 inches of precipitation, and certain valley locations in the southern interior record less than 10 inches

3   The United States Forest Service indicates a 'net volume of timber' of 202.5 billion cubic feet for the three states (Newport, et al. 1965; Wilson & Spencer 1967). British Columbia's 'mature timber volume' is a little over 268.6 billion cubic feet.

Table 5.1   Mature volume by species (billions of cubic feet)

Spruces (*Picea* species)	65.1	(24%)
Hemlock (mainly *Tsuga heterophylla*)	59.3	(22%)
Balsam (*Abies* species)	48.2	(18%)
Lodgepole pine (*Pinus contorta*)	34.7	(13%)
Western red cedar (*Thuya plicata*)	28.7	(10.5%)
Douglas fir (*Pseudotsuga menziesii*)	19.1	(7%)
Other species	13.3	(5%)

annually. Similarly, the temperature regime in parts of the southwestern coast classifies as cool-summer Mediterranean (Koeppen), while that of the northeastern interior is distinctly subarctic. The array of plant species is correspondingly varied, ranging from *Arbutus menziesii,* the only broad-leaved evergreen tree species indigenous to Canada, to *Larix lyalli* and *Pinus flexilis,* which endure the harshest of alpine conditions.[4] As such variation would imply, the distribution of the forest resource, both in species composition and in per-acre volume, shows marked regional differentiation, the contrasts from coast to interior being particularly strong.

In broad spatial terms, including non-commercial cover and immature timber, about 60 per cent of the total provincial area of 234 million acres is forested. The accompanying map (Figure 5.1) illustrates the general distribution of forest and suggests the strong influences exerted by topography, climate, and soils on that distribution. On the one hand, the major *landform* regions (see Chapter 3) are reflected in the northwestward-southeastward trending, alternate zones of forested and non-forested land. The lower, insular mountains and the associated margins of the Coastal Trough are mainly forested. The great mass of the Coast Mountains flanking the mainland coast, by contrast, is largely non-forested. Except in its northern one-third, the Interior Plateau System is essentially forested, reflecting less rugged topography and at least a thin veneer of glacially derived soil. The Columbia Mountains of southeastern British Columbia and the nearby Rocky Mountains are clearly expressed by the distribution of non-forested land on those parts of the map. The northeastern portion in turn, representing a small part of the Great Plains landforms province, is largely forested. The most extensive areas of sedentary agriculture, in the Peace River district, in the Okanagan, and in the lower reaches of the Fraser River Valley, are of little consequence in the over-

4   Acknowledgment is given to Mr R.L. Schmidt, Research Division, British Columbia Forest Service, Victoria, for suggestions concerning this portion of the manuscript.

Mature and immature timber

Other forest land

Non-forest areas

5.1
Areal Distribution of Forest Land
(derived from British Columbia Forest Service map)

all pattern of non-forested land. The major areas of open grassland in the southern part of the Interior Plateau System have similarly small effect in the general pattern.

On the other hand, in the relative sparsity of tree cover on the plateaus north of the 56th parallel and in the decreasing extent of tree cover as one progresses northward along the coast, the map suggests the broader influences of *climate* on forest distribution. In detail, it also suggests the complex interrelationships between climate, topography, and to some extent soils. From the fiordland of the coast to the valleys of the Columbia Mountains and from the 49th parallel to the northern plateaus the map reveals an intricate, interlocking pattern of wooded valleys and alpine scrub and barren land. Although not explicit on the map, similarly complex interrelationships can be said to apply in the vertical zonation of the forest and in altitude of the tree line, the latter declining from about 5500 feet above sea level in the south to perhaps 2000 feet in the north. On the coast the heaviest tree stands are associated with lower elevations, whereas in the southern interior, grassland often occurs at lower elevations. In the latter area, a prominent vegetational transition can be observed, extending from grassland in the valleys to dense forest on the plateau surfaces and to alpine scrub on the upper mountain slopes.

Location of Timber Land

Timber land, consisting of both mature and immature growth, dominates the forested land. Although the criteria for classification have changed over the years, 'timber' land supports growth of those species most utilized for sawn lumber, principally western hemlock, Douglas fir, the spruces, and the true firs. As Figure 5.1 illustrates, the largest area of 'other' forest land lies in the west-central portion of the Interior Plateau System. This consists mainly of vast stands of lodgepole pine, typically associated with sandy and gravelly glacial and glacio-fluvial deposits, and also associated with extensive forest fires in the past.

The Coast Forest (essentially the forest area west of the Coast Mountains summit-line) contains most of the remaining mature volumes of Sitka spruce, western hemlock, cedar, and Douglas fir. Although hemlock and red cedar are the co-dominant species, Douglas fir is abundant, especially in the drier, warmer areas of the south. On the coastal mainland north of latitude 51°, it is confined to rain-shadow areas which had experienced a high frequency of forest fires in pre-colonial times. Sitka spruce is most abundant on fresh alluvial soils and on lower slopes having a high moisture status. The generally mild, wet conditions that prevail on the coast promote rapid tree growth and the development of very large individual specimens. The heaviest timber stands in more accessible areas have been cut over during past logging activity, but individual old-growth trees in excess of 200 feet in height and 4 feet in diameter at the base are still encountered.

Typical interior old-growth tree stands are of smaller stature and of different species composition than those on the coast. In broad terms, the southern half of the Interior Forest contains a greater range of species and higher per-acre mature timber volumes than the northern half. Douglas fir is common south of the 53rd parallel, and although individual trees do not attain the size of their coastal counterparts, fir comprises a large share of the forest resource endowment there.[5] In the Prince George area and northward to about latitude 56°, balsam (*lasiocarpa*) fir and spruces represent the most abundant and widely used species. In the northern one-third of the province, the species mix on forested land is essentially that of the boreal forest, white spruce being the dominant conifer. Until very recently, the northern forests had not been used commercially.

Growth Potential and Forest Ownership
Two important aspects of the forest resource endowment are not shown in Figure 5.1. The first of these is propensity for forest growth, the second is ownership. Growth potential is affected by soils as a factor of site quality, but in general spatial terms, the coastal forest has a greater potential than that of the interior and, related to length of growing season, the southern forests have much greater potential than those in the north. These differences in growth potential have major long-term implications in management of the forest resource. Rotation periods necessary for regeneration of a new forest crop, and the forested area needed to support a mill of given capacity in perpetuity, differ substantially from coast to interior and from south to north. Although it is difficult to compare rotation periods because they differ with different species, the fundamental differences in biomass potential are illustrated in Table 5.2 (data are derived from *Forest Inventory Statistics,* 1969; Forest District and Coast-Interior boundaries are shown in Figure 5.2).

Ownership of the forest resource in British Columbia is largely public. Only 5 per cent of the forest area has been alienated, most of it privately held as Crown Grants. Of that portion in the public domain, about 10 per

5   The Columbia Forest, associated with the 'interior wet belt' of southeastern B.C., is rather similar to the Coast Forest, notably in species mix and per-acre volumes in old-growth stands on favourable growing sites.

Table 5.2 Average mean annual increment at culmination age, immature forest land (in cubic feet per acre)

	Productive sites	
	Good	Average
Province	51	28
Interior	48	25
Coast	114	71
Prince George Forest District	48	23
Vancouver Forest District	122	66

cent is under some form of lease or licence (mainly Tree Farm Licences) or lies within provincial parks. The fact that so large a share of the resource has remained in public ownership has made easier the initiation and application of a sustained yield programme. The extent of forest land alienation is very modest on a province-wide scale, but the proportion is much higher in the most accessible and most climatically favoured areas, averaging 20 per cent for the Vancouver Forest District and being substantially higher on Vancouver Island, which represents the most important areal component of the provincial forest resource.

RESOURCE USE – THE EXTRACTIVE PHASE

The potential value of British Columbia's bountiful timber resources was early recognized, but until external markets and transport connections to them were developed, logging was confined to the immediate vicinity of areas of settlement, mainly in the southern coastal area. By the turn of this century, logging operations had become widespread on the coast, and by 1950 had spread over much of the southern interior. Within the past decade logging has been extended into the northern forests. The provincial cut has risen to nearly two billion cubic feet annually, over half of it from coastal forests, and consists mainly of hemlock, cedar, Douglas fir, and spruce.

Historical Development

The beginnings of commercial logging in British Columbia date from the 1840s when permanent European settlement began on Vancouver Island. This settlement had an agricultural bias. Beyond the immediate needs of the establishment at Fort Victoria, there was very little market for timber or for sawn lumber and heavy forest growth was a hindrance rather than an asset. It was not until the early 1850s, when external trade linkages from Victoria to overseas markets began to develop, that logging became significant in the colonial economy.

   Because the forests were abundant and the technology of extraction was primitive, early logging sites were close to tidewater, where trees could be felled and limbed, then slid or rolled to the water whence they could be floated to the point of utilization, commonly at a nearby source of hydro-mechanical power. The advantages of tidewater for moving log supplies, and also for transporting finished products, have continued to act as important locative and integrative forces in the coastal industry. Early logging operations were centred near Victoria, but as the more accessible stands were depleted, expansion occurred toward the southwestern tip of Vancouver Island and also northward along the Island's east coast, where agricultural settlement had begun. In the early years, no commercial use was made of the vast forest resources of the mainland. Settlement and logging activity were confined to southern Vancouver Island.

   The discovery of placer gold along the alluvial bars of the lower Fraser River, and subsequently along tributary streams in the interior, gave tremendous stimulus to the colonial economy and resulted in a basic reorientation of settlement (see Chapter 2). By the mid-1860s commercial logging had extended to the mainland, particularly along the shores of Burrard Inlet, north of New Westminster. Similarly, expansion occurred on Vancouver Island, the main centres of activity appearing as isolated nodes in the most favourable areas and adjacent to sawmills. Logging technology remained comparatively primitive and log extraction remained close to tidewater.

   It was with the completion of the CPR line to Vancouver in 1886, and the associated integration of external trade connections by land and sea, that exploitation of forest resources received major impetus. By 1900 logging was rather widely dispersed in the Vancouver area, along the lower mainland coast, and along the east coastal plain of Vancouver Island. As extractive technology improved, and as readily accessible stands were cut, logging began to expand away from the coast. Primitive man-handling techniques had given way to the use of bull-teams and horse-teams, the logs being dragged along skid roads taking advantage of gravity, and moved to salt water. These in turn were being replaced by application of inanimate energy. Because of the large size of individual logs and because of the youthful nature and flashy characteristics of most coastal streams, rivers were not used as a medium of transport.

During the first quarter of this century, forestry emerged as the linch-pin of the provincial economy and the pattern of logging activity ex-panded along both margins of the Strait of Georgia and northward to the northern end of Vancouver Island. The industry remained heavily oriented to the southwest coast, though commercial use of interior stands had begun along the Canadian Pacific and Grand Trunk (Canadian Na-tional) rail lines. Logging continued to be spatially associated with saw-milling but the introduction of newer means of log transport permitted a greater separation, so that logging camps were established at some dis-tance from milling sites. Especially on Vancouver Island, logging camps operated well inland from tidewater. The combination of amenable to-pography, high quality, and high volume of timber stands on the Island, coupled with the introduction of the steam-engine and logging railway, facilitated the separation. This growing spatial dissociation contributed to the development of large-capacity, fixed mills that could draw upon a large resource hinterland for their continuing operation.

The trend that had become clearly established on the coast in the 1920s has continued to the present. With the gradual evolution of major cor-porate control in the industry, milling has tended to become centralized but logging has expanded areally. Even the timber resources of the Queen Charlotte Islands, over 500 miles from centres of utilization in the lower mainland, have been tapped. On Vancouver Island, logging crews operate far inland from the coast and cutting has been extended into the head-water areas of streams. In the post-war period, the logging railway has given way to truck roads, many of which use old railway grades, but ex-tend log transport into more difficult terrain.

Log Extraction and Transport

As one might expect, most of the innovative logging techniques that have appeared in the Pacific Northwest are especially adapted to mountainous topography. Among the many cable-hauling systems that have been de-veloped for skidding logs from growing site to truck-loading point, the self-mobile or 'portable' spar tree is the most extensively used in the coastal industry. Depending on local topography, such a system can be moved to a setting and can yard logs from distances up to about a fifth of a mile with high productivity per man-hour.

Individual logging settings are linked with log dumping points by an intricate pattern of main and secondary haul roads. Typically, the road networks are built and maintained on their holdings by the timber com-panies and consequently they can be designed and engineered for off-highway vehicles carrying loads well in excess of provincial highway standards.

From log dump to mill site the form of transport varies with distance and sea conditions. In the comparatively sheltered waters between Vancouver Island and the mainland coast, the logs are usually towed in flat rafts to booming grounds or temporary log storage areas near the points of utilization. From more distant points and across exposed waters, self-loading and self-dumping log carriers are now employed. These vehicles have the advantages of large capacity and low 'turn-around' time. The above examples of log extraction and log transport methods used on the coast suggest the present scale of the extractive phase. Indirectly, they also suggest the tremendous influence that developing technology continues to exert upon the spatial expression of the industry.

Logging in the interior differs in character from that on the coast. The differences are in part related to the different species composition of the forests, smaller sizes of individual trees, lower per-acre volumes of usable timber, more moderate slopes, and different transport linkages. Most interior logging has taken place within the past 25 years. Early in the post-war period, and continuing into the 1960s, logging was essentially selective, only those trees that had value for lumber being taken. Individual trees were felled and the logs hauled to nearby points of utilization by caterpillar tractor. Until the recent introduction of portable spar trees and clear-cutting practices, the cable-hauling systems typical of the coastal phase of the industry were not used.

Formerly, logs were drawn comparatively short distances from forest areas to nearby portable mills for conversion to sawn lumber. Fundamental changes are occurring in the spatial organization of the industry and logs are now hauled by truck from broad forest tracts to widely dispersed, more permanent mill sites.

Differences in the nature and distribution of the resource endowment between coast and interior have given rise to differences in the conduct of the industry, but it can be said that similar changes in the spatial expression of logging and log transport have occurred. Those that took place on the coast over a span of 100 years have been repeated in the interior within the space of 25. It should be stressed, however, that interior log transport has no counterpart to the salt-water sorting and hauling typical of the coast. Logs are boomed and rafted on some of the larger lakes, but with few exceptions rivers are not used as a transport medium and logs must be moved over the provincial road system to points of utilization. This carries the implication of high transport costs and the need to conform to provincial highway load limits.

Annual Cut

The 1970 annual log harvest in British Columbia approached two billion cubic feet, over half of it coming from the coast.[6] This is about 56 per cent of the 'possible allowable annual cut' (all species) under the terms of the continuous forest inventory of British Columbia. Expressed as sawn lumber equivalent, the total yield in 1970 was approximately eight billion board feet, sufficient to build nearly one million wood-frame homes. Industrial demands have been such that the total harvest has increased markedly, rising from about one billion cubic feet in 1959 to one-and-a-half billion in 1964, and it is expected to reach two billion in 1971.

Almost all of the log harvest is processed in British Columbia mills, sawmills taking about 75 per cent of the total. The particular requirements of the sawmills, therefore, largely determine the species mix in that harvest. Some species are more desirable than others for lumber manufacture. Consequently the proportion of an individual species in the annual cut tends to differ from the proportion of that species in the total mature forest volume. The discrepancy is particularly apparent in the case of Douglas fir. Up to 1960 this prime species comprised at least one-third of the total annual cut, and up to 1967 continued to account for the largest single share. Yet the remaining stands of Douglas fir make up less than 7 per cent of the mature forest volume. Reforestation and other silvicultural practices might ultimately change the situation, but for the next 25 years it seems likely that Douglas fir will figure much less prominently in B.C.'s forest industry than has been traditional in the past. The annual cuts of both hemlock and spruce now exceed that of fir. This is a reflection of the declining availability of Douglas fir and also of the substitution of other species for sawn lumber and pulp. Party because of the rapid post-war growth of the interior forest industry, the fir cut there began to exceed that on the coast, but the trend was not sustained. In each year since 1963 most of the Douglas fir cut has come from the coast. In view of the relative resource endowment, this is not surprising; 56 per cent of the mature fir volume in British Columbia is within coastal forests.

The 1969 cut by forest district and by species is represented in Figure 5.2. Since the size of the map symbols is directly proportional to the vol-

6   The 1970 *Annual Report* of the British Columbia Forest Service lists a total cut, all products, of 1.933 billion cubic feet, of which 1.018 billion came from coast operations. Under the standards of close utilization that now apply in the industry, the total roundwood cut includes a substantial amount of material unsuited to sawmilling; hence total volumes are usually expressed in cubic feet rather than board-foot measure. The coast-interior boundary adopted by the B.C. Forest Service is represented in Figure 5.2. References to data for coast and interior are based upon the Forest Service definition.

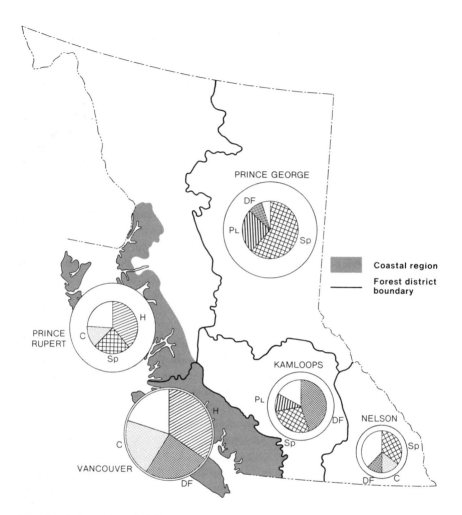

Diameter of pie graph symbols is proportional to volume of cut for each forest district.
Inner circle represents 1969 cut. Outer circle represents possible allowable cut.
Size of pie graph segments is proportional to species cut, by forest district.

Major species are represented as follows:

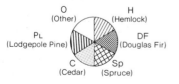

O
(Other)
H
(Hemlock)
PL
(Lodgepole Pine)
DF
(Douglas Fir)
C
(Cedar)
Sp
(Spruce)

Thousands of cubic metres

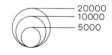

20000
10000
5000

5.2
Present and Potential Forest Harvest
(derived from Annual Report of British Columbia Forest Service, 1970, and Forest Inventory Statistics of British Columbia, 1969)

ume of cut, the comparative importance of the Vancouver Forest District is apparent. Although it is one of the smallest in forested area, its cut approaches half of the provincial total. As suggested by the map symbols showing the potential cut, however, the present cut in the Vancouver District is close to the possible allowable annual cut if all private and publicly held forest land (excluding parks) were under sustained yield management at close utilization standards. Thus it seems unlikely that the Vancouver Forest District can indefinitely retain its pre-eminent position if the forest industry continues to expand in other parts of the province. Such expansion has been occurring very rapidly in the Prince George Forest District, which, in 1969, ranked second in volume of cut but accounted for less than half that from the Vancouver District. The forested area in the Prince George District is so vast (larger than the combined areas of Great Britain and Northern Ireland) that the possible allowable annual cut is 10 per cent greater than that from the southwest coast. Similarly, the Prince Rupert Forest District, at present accounting for about 15 per cent of the annual cut, has a large potential still to be realized, the possible allowable annual cut being approximately the same as that of the Vancouver District. It should be emphasized that considerably more than half of the present cut and one-third of the potential cut in the Prince Rupert District are contributed by the coastal portion. As the map shows, the present cut from the Kamloops District is about the same as that from Prince Rupert, but the possible allowable cut is little better than half as great. The Nelson Forest District, in the southeast, has the smallest area of forest land, the smallest cut, and the smallest potential. On a unit-area basis, however, both Kamloops and Nelson have higher productivity than the Prince George District, reflecting the differences in biomass potential.

As outlined in the preceding section, there are considerable differences between the forest districts in major species cut. These differences are portrayed by the pie graphs in Figure 5.2. Hemlock, Douglas fir, and cedar make up over three-quarters of the cut in the Vancouver district, and hemlock, spruce, and cedar account for most of the cut from the Prince Rupert District. In the interior, the resource endowment is reflected in the relative proportions of spruce and Douglas fir cut. Spruce accounts for over two-thirds of the total in the Prince George District, most of the remainder being lodgepole pine. In the Nelson Forest District, spruce accounts for about one-third of the cut, with a variety of other species including cedar and hemlock contributing the remainder. In the Kamloops District, by contrast, Douglas fir continues to provide by far the greatest single share, spruce being of secondary importance. The fact that, throughout its natural range, so large a share is made up of Douglas fir attests to the commercial desirability of that species.

The Coast Forest at present contributes well over half of the annual cut. Although it constitutes only one-sixth of the provincial forested area, it contains over 42 per cent of the net forest volume. As the resource demands of industry increase, however, one can anticipate that the cut will approach the total forest potential for each forest district and that all species will be utilized in one form or another. As this comes about, a basic change can be expected in the regional pattern of cut. Because the total possible allowable cut from interior forests is double that from the coast, it is probable that the interior contribution will proportionately increase. Based upon known potential, the increase would come mainly from the northern two-thirds of the province. Cut projections of this sort would, of course, assume that the widely dispersed forests of the northern interior were made accessible, for at present they are essentially remote and untapped. If major changes in regional cut do occur, related changes in the pattern of milling activity might follow. But by the time growth potential and annual cut are brought into balance, the relative efficiency of transport linkages might be such as to perpetuate the present pattern. In such speculation it is appropriate to consider the possible longer-term effects of more intensive forest management, including selective tree breeding, large-scale reforestation, and soil fertilization. Experiments conducted in the Pacific Northwest and elsewhere have demonstrated that with selective breeding and careful management it is possible to lower the rotation period for Douglas fir on favourable growing sites by about two-thirds. The geographic implications of such advances in forest biology and silviculture are considerable. In spatial terms, they would appear to have their greatest expression where growth potential is highest so that, in the long-term future, the Vancouver Forest District might well attain a relative importance far beyond that indicated by the allowable cut statistics now available.

RESOURCE USE – SAWMILLING

Sawmilling is the traditional conversion enterprise, and in the century and a quarter that has elapsed since its commercial beginnings in British Columbia, sawmilling has become ubiquitous. From the coast to the Interior Plains and from metropolitan areas to rural hamlets, it would be difficult to find a community in the province whose economic base is not to some extent dependent upon sawmilling. In the more industrially developed areas, and especially on the coast, process integration has made sawmills more efficient, but the 'beehive' waste burner, once the hallmark of sawmilling in the northwest, is still very much a part of the rural landscape. Despite the dramatic growth in other sectors of the forest industry, sawmilling and shingle-milling continue to account for over one-third of the net value of all wood processing in British Columbia.[7]

Pattern of Evolution on the Coast

Like logging, commercial sawmilling had its beginnings in British Columbia near Victoria and spread northwestward from there. Another node of sawmilling was in existence near Vancouver before the CPR line reached the coast in 1886. The latter node grew rapidly, but has remained remarkably consistent in general location though experiencing internal spatial change. With minor exceptions, no extension of sawmilling has taken place either eastward in the Fraser Valley or northwestward along the mainland coast. This consistency of milling location in the Vancouver area is related to the comparative ease with which logs can be rafted in the Strait of Georgia and in the semitidal reaches of the lower Fraser River and its north-side tributaries. The availability of suitable mill sites in Vancouver's commodious harbour and in sheltered waters nearby has also had an important centralizing influence. On the other hand, the general sparsity of sawmilling northward along the coast may be accounted for by two interacting factors: the limited resource hinterland, and the absence of opportunity for integration of rail and sea export routes there. For over 200 miles, the generally rugged and heavily fiorded coast beyond Powell River is accessible only by sea and air.

The pattern of sawmilling on Vancouver Island is less strongly concentrated. From an early nucleus in the south it spread to timber-rich areas between Victoria and Nanaimo, particularly in the Chemainus and Cowichan areas.[8] Other mill concentrations developed at or near the head of Alberni Inlet, a fiord channel that all but bifurcates Vancouver Island. By the 1930s sawmills were located at many points along the east coastal lowland of the Island south of Campbell River, but showed major clusterings in the Port Alberni area, in the Cowichan-Chemainus vicinity, and at Victoria. North of Campbell River access was more difficult and milling

7 'Wood processing' includes sawmilling, pulp- and paper-milling, veneer and plywood manufacture, sash and door production, the manufacture of furniture and fixtures, boxes, bags, and paper, and other wood- and paper-using industries.
8 See Figure 5.5. The Chemainus and Cowichan sawmilling centres are within 20 miles of the pulp-mill at Crofton, Campbell River is near Duncan Bay, and the Nimpkish Valley lies east of Port Alice.

was limited to a single node at the mouth of the broad and heavily timbered Nimpkish valley.[9] The general distributional pattern that had developed early has tended to persist. Changes have occurred, especially in the relative importance of individual mills and in the number of mills operating, but the concentrations around Victoria, Cowichan-Chemainus, and Port Alberni are prominent. North and west of Campbell River the only major sawmill is located on the west coast of the Island at Tahsis, near historic Nootka Sound. Considering the quality and quantity of its timber resources and their growth potential, it is not surprising that the two largest-capacity sawmills now operating in British Columbia are both on southern Vancouver Island.

Early mill locations were associated not only with the proximity of readily exploitable timber and of salt-water transport, but also with tidewater sites at which hydro-mechanical power could be developed. Although providing the great advantages of simplicity, durability, and minimal cost, suitable hydro-mechanical power sites are scarce. Their locative constraints encouraged application of other forms of inanimate energy, notably steam. Transport linkages in moving logs to mills and sawn lumber to export markets continue to exercise strong influences on mill location, however, so that sheltered, tidewater sites or those with short-haul road and rail connections to deep-sea loading facilities are characteristic of the industry. It is still common for ocean-going vessels to call at several different mill sites when making up cargo destined for overseas markets. The sawmilling locations that have persisted through time are those that have been strategically well-located with respect to timber supplies and to the assembly of those supplies at the mill site. Those that were able to command large resource areas, either through private ownership or under licence from the government, have become more dominant. Further, the integration of different milling activities at these dominant sites has tended to stabilize the locational pattern.

Sustained Yield

Characteristically, the mills on Vancouver Island and on the southern mainland coast are of large capacity and individually represent a capital investment of millions of dollars. Including hydraulic barker, headrig, and other machinery and buildings, a large coastal sawmill would represent a capital investment of perhaps 4½ to 5 million dollars and would employ 45 to 50 men. In order to justify this magnitude of investment,

9 A sawmill had been built at Port Alice but became part of the early pulp mill operation there.

daily operation and process integration are desirable and raw material supplies must be assured. The policy of sustained yield forestry that the British Columbia government adopted in 1953 has done much to ensure a continuing log supply. Intensive competition for what was ultimately recognized as a limited raw material base led to a situation in which short-term investments and quick returns were expected and a 'cut out and get out' attitude engendered. Recognizing the long-term implications for the British Columbia economy, the government took action to set standards for utilization, to exercise stronger controls on the allocation of cutting rights on public lands, and to implement a sustained-yield programme.

Under the policy, two broad categories of forest management have been established. The first is the Tree Farm Licence, designed to encourage established industries to practise sustained-yield forestry, the major incentive being the allocation of public timberlands to the company in perpetuity. Sustained-yield practices, fire protection, disease and pest control, and access must be maintained. The other form of management is the Public Sustained Yield Unit under which the B.C. Forest Service maintains direct control and determines when a given block of timber is ready for cutting. The cutting rights are normally decided on the basis of timber auction. Most of the Tree Farm Licences are located in the Vancouver and Prince Rupert forest districts; most of the PSYUs are in the interior. In the two decades since initiation of the policy, sustained-yield management has been extended to all but the most northerly of British Columbia's forested lands. There can be little doubt but that this achievement will help to stabilize the industry as a whole.

Pattern of Evolution in the Interior
Sawmilling in the interior had its commercial beginnings some time later than on the Pacific seaboard, developing in conjunction with the Canadian Pacific Railway main line across southern British Columbia.[10] The real economic impact of the railway upon interior sawmilling was associated with the settlement boom on the Canadian prairies in the first decade of the twentieth century. Because of the rail haulage to the coast and transshipment necessary, interior lumber producers had not been able to compete effectively in foreign export markets. Domestic markets on the prairies opened new horizons to interior mills. The need for prod-

---

10   A considerable number of mills were built during the 1880s and 1890s in southeastern B.C. A few of them are reported to have had capacities in excess of 100,000 board feet a day, but as a result of indiscriminate cutting and wasteful practices, the forest resources available to support them were soon depleted.

uct quality and the need to locate close to the rail line limited the areas within which sawmills could economically operate. The strip from Kamloops to Revelstoke, in the 'interior wet belt' and immediately tributary to Shuswap Lake, was one of the best endowed. The finest timber stands there compared favourably with those on the coast and advantage could be taken of water transport in moving the logs. The market demand associated with the prairie settlement boom was short-lived, for by the beginning of World War I Canada was facing a severe economic depression. Following the war, markets expanded somewhat, and a modest northward component was added to the pattern of interior milling. Completion of the Grand Trunk (Canadian National) rail line to Prince Rupert in 1914 and to Vancouver in 1915 added a new dimension to transport connectivity. Except for the Yellowhead–Prince George and Yellowhead–Kamloops sections, however, the line did not tap any new forest resources for which there was high demand. The lumber industry in British Columbia was based upon Douglas fir, and westward from Prince George, that species is comparatively sparse. The provincially owned Pacific Great Eastern Railway,[11] on the other hand, was extended through potential timber land but until the 1950s it had no direct connection with either transcontinental line. Hence its early impact upon the spatial pattern of interior sawmilling was comparatively small.

Expansion of the interior industry was more apparent in the south where Douglas fir is more widespread, but even there total mill capacity remained far smaller than on the coast. In the decade before World War II lumber markets in the continental interior were less than encouraging, and despite the availability of rail access, sawmilling was in a period of near-stagnation. Lumber demands related to wartime construction in the 1940s, the rapidly expanding domestic and foreign wood products market that ensued, and the emergence of truck transport as an active competitor to rail haul had far-reaching impact upon the relative importance and distribution of sawmilling in interior British Columbia. By 1950 hundreds of mills, most of them small, portable units, had come into existence along the main transport routes.[12]

Interior mills are of two basic types, stationary and portable. The former is in some respects not unlike that of the coast. Aside from fixed location it has moderate to high daily capacity and draws log supplies

11 In April 1972, the Pacific Great Eastern Railway was renamed the British Columbia Railway.
12 In 1955 there were nearly 2500 operating sawmills in the province, all but about 350 of them in the interior. The 350 coast mills produced about 60 per cent of the sawn lumber cut in that year.

from a large tributary area. Such mills are typically sited along the main transport routes, prominent nodes being associated with the CNR lines from Yellowhead Pass to Prince Rupert and to Kamloops, the PGE (British Columbia Railway) from Fort St John to Squamish, and the CPR route from Revelstoke to Vancouver. Other nodes appear in the southern Rocky Mountain Trench and through the 'boundary country' of south-central British Columbia. In most instances, logs are moved to the mill by truck and the finished product is shipped out by rail. Most of the larger mills convert lumber waste to pulp chips, which are used at site in integrated complexes or, more commonly, moved by rail to pulp-mills elsewhere.

The portable mills are far more numerous but are very different in sawn-lumber capacity, employment, and capital investment requirements as well as in raw material handling and product flows. The market situation that prevailed for mills in the interior of British Columbia from the mid-1940s to the mid-1960s was one heavily favouring the production of sawn lumber. Because of the nature and distribution of the forest resource there, logging tended to be selective, but the forest area available for exploitation was vast. Under those circumstances, the diesel-driven, portable sawmill was a well-suited conversion device. It took little capital to acquire and operate, its labour inputs per unit of output were not excessive, it could be moved to the resource, and it was admirably suited to backwoods transport conditions. Many individuals, who had had little previous connection with logging and sawmilling, were able to earn handsome profits. The economic impact reverberated through interior communities. The proliferation of bush mills did not long endure, however, and by the early 1960s change had already set in. The lumber market was becoming more competitive, costs were spiralling, and cutting rights to suitable timber stands were hard to acquire. As had been demonstrated on the coast a quarter-century earlier, managerial skill, resource control, and strategic location with respect to raw materials and markets were the determinants of success or failure.

By the mid-1960s the number of sawmills operating in the interior had dropped to about 1000; by 1970 it had further declined to less than 900. Assuming that small operations can continue to acquire timber, either on farm woodlots or on other private holdings, it is likely that portable sawmilling will continue to be associated with the interior industry, but on a much more limited scale. Most of the lumber output from the interior will centre on the larger, stationary mills, whose efficiencies in raw material conversion are much higher and whose capacities have grown in recent years to rival those on the coast.

Rapid growth in other sectors of forest utilization, especially pulp-mill-

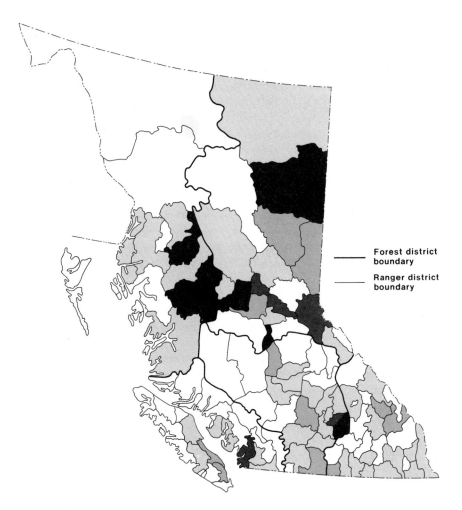

Forest district
boundary

Ranger district
boundary

Number of mills

Less than 7

7-18

19-25

26-33

Over 33

5.3
Number of Sawmills (by Ranger District), 1970
(derived from British Columbia Forest Service data)

ing, is encouraging vertical and horizontal integration of the industry. One locational outcome of such internal change could be an increasing centralization of the forest industry in existing major nodes. As described below, however, new forest industrial complexes are envisioned to utilize now undeveloped forest resources in northern British Columbia. Thus a dual spatial expression of current forces of change can be conjectured: increasing centralization in existing interior nodes and northward expansion into a few new ones. Whatever the long-term outcome may be, it seems probable that, for the next decade at least, the distributional pattern of interior sawmilling will continue to show much less spatial concentration than that on the coast.

Number of Mills and Mill Capacity

Regional differences in the number and capacity of sawmills are portrayed in Figures 5.3 and 5.4. The former illustrates the number of mills (excluding combined saw- and shingle-mills) by forest ranger district. Although the districts are far from uniform in area, the size variation tends to be latitudinal. It is apparent from the map that in general the interior ranger districts have many more mills than those on the coast. The map also shows the areas of mill concentration, which reflect the basic transport pattern as much as they do the forest resource distribution. The Peace River region, one of the larger agricultural regions in the province, is shown to be one such area of mill concentration. The apparent anomaly is easily explained. Farm woodlot enterprises are a common adjunct of farming there and small, portable mills are often associated with them.

Further insight into the distinction between coast and interior sawmilling is offered in Figure 5.4. This map represents the average daily capacity of all operating sawmills expressed in thousands of board feet (M.B.M.). Both map and inset reveal that Vancouver Island and the Vancouver–New Westminster area have the greatest concentration of large-capacity mills. Only the Aleza Lake Ranger District, immediately east of Prince George, has a comparable capacity. As the inset shows, however, large mills now exist in the interior, their distributional pattern being strongly oriented to the railways.

PULP AND PAPER MILLING

Basic and far-reaching change has characterized British Columbia's industrial development within the past decade (see Chapter 4). Nowhere is the change more apparent, nor the long-term implications more dramatic, than in the pulp and paper industry. In the decade 1959–69, pulp production

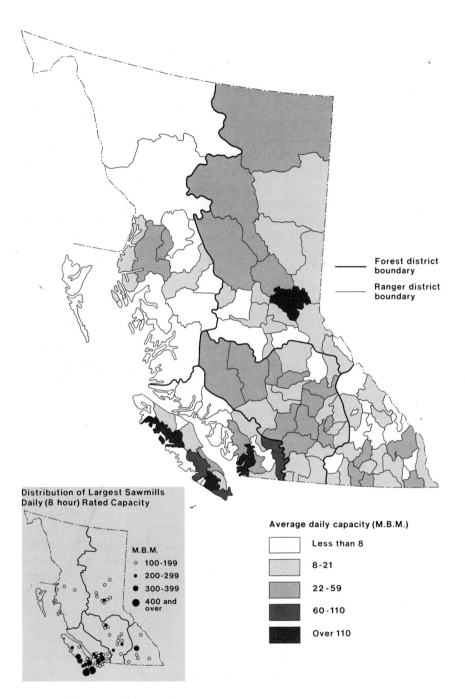

Forest district
boundary

Ranger district
boundary

**Distribution of Largest Sawmills
Daily (8 hour) Rated Capacity**

M.B.M.
○ 100-199
● 200-299
● 300-399
● 400 and
  over

Average daily capacity (M.B.M.)

Less than 8

8-21

22-59

60-110

Over 110

**5.4
Capacity of Sawmills (by Ranger District), 1970
(derived from British Columbia Forest Service data)**

rose from less than two million to nearly five million tons annually. British Columbia now accounts for over one-quarter of the national output of pulp and about 4½ per cent of the world total. Provincially, the pulp and paper industry vies with sawmilling in net production value, individually outranking any other resource-based industry except mining, but engaging less than 25 per cent of the direct employment in British Columbia's forest industry.[13] Unlike its eastern Canadian counterpart, much of whose production is destined for tariff-free newsprint markets in the United States, pulp and paper milling in British Columbia is based mainly on the conversion of wood to chemical pulp. By tonnage, the annual output of paper is little more than one-third that of pulp (*Financial and Economic Review*, Table 25).

Early Mill Sites and Areal Expansion

Historically the industry has centred on the coast. An abortive beginning was made in 1894 when a mechanical conversion mill, using rags and sacking as raw material, commenced operation at Port Alberni (see Figure 5.5). By 1910 two new mills had been built, one at Port Mellon and the other at Powell River, on the Strait of Georgia. At the latter site a remarkably convenient source of waterpower was linked to wood-grinding machinery to derive mechanical pulp or ground-wood, a major ingredient in newsprint. Newsprint has continued to figure prominently in its output and Powell River currently produces far more of it than any other mill in the province.

Within a decade new mills were established at Woodfibre, near the head of Howe Sound, at Ocean Falls, about mid-point on the mainland coast, and at Port Alice on northern Vancouver Island. In the period of expansion a pulp-mill was built at Swanson Bay, northwest of Ocean Falls, but production was intermittent and the mill had closed by 1918. Completion of these plants established a pattern of pulp and paper mills in British Columbia that was unchanged for a quarter of a century. Expansion took place at existing plants, but no new mills were built in the province until after World War II. In each case, energy availability, tidewater access, an abundant supply of chemically soft, fresh water, and nearby roundwood sources were important siting factors. Because markets and most input supplies were external, tidewater location was particularly important. Though all but the Port Alice plant used hydro-mechanical power, all five

13 The Dominion Bureau of Statistics indicates value added by industry (British Columbia) in 1967 as follows (values have been rounded): sawmills and planing mills, $257 million; pulp and paper mills, $227 million; mineral industries, $241 million.

relied upon the generation of additional energy requirements, especially for the electricity and heat needed in chemical pulping. This was developed in at-site thermal plants, the energy source for which was heavy distillates of petroleum, mainly from California. Similarly for chemical supplies, the dependence was entirely upon waterborne traffic. Both the mills and the small communities that huddled around them were essentially isolated, externally dependent company operations, linked by sea to the outside world.

Post-war Changes

By 1945 the forces of change were at work. Not only was there a sharp increase in market demand for forest products, but also the pressure of existing industry on available wood supplies was being felt. The possibilities and potential advantages of integrating pulp and paper making with sawmilling were being recognized. Waste wood from the sawmills could be converted to chips to feed the pulp-mills, and sawdust and log bark could be used to fire plant boilers to generate electrical power and steam.[14] Because of the advantages of spatial proximity, most new mills that were built in the post-war period to 1956 were located near existing coast sawmills – at Crofton (north of Victoria), Port Alberni, Nanaimo, Duncan Bay (near Campbell River), and Prince Rupert. Only one pulp-mill was under development by 1956 in the interior and it, in turn, was closely associated with a sawmilling complex. In the same way that sheltered coastal waterways, and particularly the Strait of Georgia, provide a convenient, low-cost transport medium for log rafts, so they are used in the movement of chip scows and fuel scows from sawmill to pulp-mill. Considerable volumes of chips are needed and with expanding plant capacity the chip scow has become almost as common a sight in south coast waters as the traditional log raft. So important has the conversion of sawmill and plywood plant residue become that over half the current pulp-mill requirement is met from wood residue; less than 15 per cent of the forest cut goes directly to pulp-mills. Other advantages of integration relate to product diversification among plants under single corporate control, so that, within the over-all limits of market demand, it is possible for individual mills to emphasize a particular product.

14   The mixture of bark (from hydraulic log-barkers), sawdust, and dust from the planers is generally referred to as 'hog fuel.' The output from a large coastal sawmill is sufficient to generate most of the mill's internal energy requirements and provide a surplus that could be channelled to a pulp-mill. Because hog fuel has a high moisture content, petroleum is usually used as a supplement. Latterly sawdust is being used for pulping, rather than as a component of hog fuel.

The pre-war structure of the industry emphasized newsprint and sulphite pulp, destined mainly for markets in the United States. In those markets the pulp demand was mainly for dissolving grades of sulphite which was then used in the production of such derived products as rayon and acetate yarns, cellophane, and explosives. The rapid growth in post-war markets brought a change in market emphasis. Demand continued for sulphite pulp to feed chemical industries in export areas, but most of the demand was for pulp to be used in the secondary manufacture of paper products. A revolution in the use of paper for food packaging, corrugated cartons, and multi-wall bags vastly increased the requirement for a 'strength' pulp. This shift in market emphasis, coupled with advancing technology, encouraged application of the long-known 'kraft' or sulphate process. Virtually all new plant capacity and expansion of existing plants after World War II was designed to produce sulphate pulp. In general, the kraft process is better adapted to handling a diversity of wood species, including the pines and Douglas fir.

Wood and Water – Prime Location Factors
Until 1961, all pulp produced in British Columbia came from coast mills and only one mill was under construction in the interior. By that date there were 10 primary mills on the coast whose combined annual production reached 2¼ million tons of pulp and well over 1 million tons of paper. Many reasons can be advanced to account for this heavy concentration in the coastal area. Among the more important of these are raw material supplies, low-cost water transport, and waste-disposal opportunities. Chief among raw material supplies are wood and water. The coastal species most used for lumber – hemlock, Douglas fir, and cedar – are highly suited for pulping by the kraft process. Their respective ratios of chip input to pulp yield vary somewhat, as do their 'cooking' requirements, but all result in a high-strength, long-fibre pulp that is in demand in world markets. The opportunities on the coast not only for process integration but also for large-scale production have been important locative forces. Coupled with the long-term prospect of assured roundwood supplies and a high growth potential, they will continue to provide a strong propellant to the coastal industry.

Pulp and paper making is a water-intensive process and the low-cost availability of large volumes of sediment-free, chemically soft water has long favoured coastal sites. Depending on the process and the cost and availability of water, between 35,000 and 55,000 gallons of water are used per ton of pulp. Actual water consumption in pulping is very small. Most of the input is lost to the effluent sewers as a result of washing the pulp. A mill of 500 tons-per-day capacity uses upwards of 100,000 tons or 20 million gallons of water every day. This is more than enough to supply the domestic requirements of a city of 100,000 people. Some coast mills use far in excess of this amount.

Coastal location has not only provided the advantage of abundant water availability but also that of convenient effluent disposal. Waste water contains a significant amount of chemicals and cellulose, the recovery of which is not economically feasible given the availability of low-cost water and the fact that there is little or no constraint on effluent discharge. Mill effluent, especially from the sulphite process, has a high biochemical oxygen demand, but in the past it has been considered that tidewater disposal would cause no pollution problem except in highly localized areas. Latterly, especially in waters adjacent to the Strait of Georgia, serious questions are being raised concerning loss of environmental quality as a result of atmospheric and marine pollution from pulp-mills. Substantially greater recycling of input water is possible, but the greater the degree of recycling necessary, the lower the cost advantage will be in favour of coastal location. In comparison with the effluent problems and constraints associated with the interior, however, those of coastal mills are still comparatively small.

Just as tidewater has been advantageous in effluent disposal, so it has long been of critical importance in the transport of raw materials to the mill and in the shipment of finished products from it. The comparative ease with which this can be done, and the opportunities for mechanization, are such as to provide a distinct cost advantage. For these various reasons, the traditional core of British Columbia's pulp and paper industry is unlikely to be supplanted, in spite of the dramatic expansion to interior forests within the past decade. Even including the mills under construction in 1970, total primary capacity on the coast was still two and one-half times greater than that of interior mills – a clear reflection of the locational advantages of the coast.

Expansion in the Interior
The accompanying map (Figure 5.5) shows the distribution of pulp and paper mills in 1971. Both primary and secondary (tissue and packaging) plants are represented. Because of the diversity of products and planned expansions, capacity is not shown. The largest coast mills, at Powell River, Port Alberni, Duncan Bay, and Crofton, are individually far larger than anything existing or planned for the interior.

By 1961, only the mill at Castlegar had been built. In 1971, out of a total of 25 plants operating or under construction, 9 were non-coastal. Most of the potential sites under investigation also lie in the interior. Clearly, a completely new dimension had been added to the spatial pattern of the industry, a dimension that will be augmented as additional forest resources are allocated.

The change can be accounted for by a combination of propellants. Chief among them has been the availability of low-cost wood chips and government allocation of roundwood under a sustained yield programme. Through tenure conditions under the general sustained yield programme and by regional adjustment of stumpage values, the provincial government has provided special inducements to interior producers. These inducements, coupled with a surplus of wood residue from existing sawmill complexes, have meant appreciably lower wood chip costs to interior pulp-mills than to coast mills. Further, a continuing chip supply is virtually guaranteed. Other important factors have been the availability of investment capital and the increasing world demand for pulp and paper.

Just as had happened on the coast, many interior sawmills have been economically rejuvenated as a result of the opportunity to sell residue chips to the pulp-mills. This has added stability to the forest industry and has also tended to centralize it in the major existing nodes. The impact on regional economies has been tremendous (see Chapter 4). Prince George, in particular, has become a boom town that now vies with Kamloops as the largest urban centre in the interior.

Not only has the impact been felt in existing population centres; completely new ('instant') communities have been established both in the interior and on the coast, perhaps the outstanding example of which is Mackenzie, created in 1965 near the southern edge of the giant Peace River reservoir.[15] The community is linked to the PGE (B.C. Railway) line and to the Hart highway connecting Prince George with the Peace River country, and the reservoir itself has given access to a vast area of timber in the northern Rocky Mountain Trench.

Future Possibilities

In many ways the establishment of a sawmilling and pulp and paper milling complex at Mackenzie epitomizes the expanding development of British Columbia's northern forest resources. The provincial government

15 In 1966 Mackenzie reported a population of 111. The 1971 census recorded 2400. Sawmills were built in the first stage of development and in December 1970 the first pulp-mill went on stream. A second pulp-mill is expected to start production in the fall of 1972.

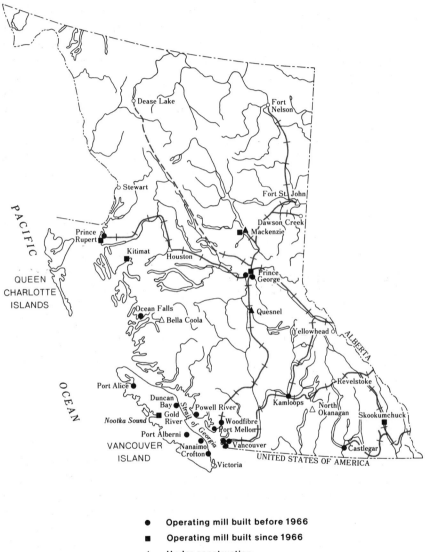

5.5
Pulp and Paper Mills, 1971
(derived from Province of British Columbia Budget Speech, 1971)

has actively encouraged resource development there by extending railway trackage and by road construction. Given practicable rail or water-and-rail access, it seems inevitable that further resource exploitation will occur. Forestry officials have indicated a sufficient roundwood supply in northern B.C. to support several new mills.[16] Including all species, the northern forested area west of the Rocky Mountain Trench is estimated to yield an annual allowable cut of 160 million cubic feet – sufficient to feed at least two mills.[17] The northeastern part of the province is believed to have enough timber to support another three or four mills (estimated annual allowable cut 200 million cubic feet). It would be overly sanguine, however, to predict the appearance of even five new pulp-mills on the basis of total roundwood supply even if there was sufficient market demand. Timber in the north is 'patchy,' having high variability from one location to another, and is spread over a vast area to which there is at present very little or no ground transport connection. Even the B.C. Railway link to Fort Nelson, recently completed, and the planned extension to Dease Lake will provide only limited forest access. Further, the added rail hauls would represent a cost disadvantage, so that special inducements would probably be necessary to encourage industrial development. Aside from this, the rigorous winter conditions, relative isolation, and lack of amenities would make difficult the recruitment of a stable labour force. It would appear that, over the next decade, development of the forest industry in northern B.C. will more likely be associated with the Fort Nelson basin than with the area west of the Rocky Mountain Trench.

OTHER FOREST PRODUCTS

Industrially, Canadians have been cast in the role of raw material producers and nowhere is this more apparent than in British Columbia. Economic viability is heavily dependent upon external markets in highly industrialized countries whose requirements are for raw or semiprocessed resources. In line with the growing population and a rapidly advancing standard of living, Canadian domestic markets are expanding, and for a few forest products British Columbia producers can sell much of the out-

16 Grateful acknowledgment is given to Mr W.G. Hughes, Management Division, and to Mr W.E.L. Young, Inventory Division, B.C. Forest Service, for their suggestions and insights concerning the present development and future potential of B.C.'s forests.
17 Economies of scale are of increasing importance in pulp and paper milling. In general, capacities of at least 800 tons per day are now considered desirable to maintain a strong competitive position.

put nationally. But even in the plywood industry foreign countries take a substantial part of the output. In 1969, for example, nearly all of the cedar shingles and shakes, over 70 per cent of the lumber, most of the pulp and paper, and one-quarter of the plywood produced were shipped to foreign markets. There has been a modest but growing trend, however, toward more advanced processing prior to marketing. Examples may be cited in the plywood and particle board industry and container manufacture. Particle board has only recently been produced in the province and has a promising Canadian market in residential construction. Processing of paperboard, corrugating materials, multi-wall bags, and similar products has grown in response to the packaging revolution. Process integration, along with the output of a highly desirable 'strength' product, has allowed British Columbia producers to take advantage of the domestic market opportunity. Canadian per-capita consumption of paper and paperboard now ranks among the three highest in the world. It is with the construction-grade plywood industry, though, that British Columbia's production advantages are most apparent.

The Plywood Industry
The Canadian plywood industry began early on the west coast, based upon the availability of large-diameter, straight-grained, Douglas fir peeler logs. The first mill was erected in 1913 in the Vancouver area, but it was not until the mid-1930s that a large-scale mill was built. By 1945 there were nine plywood mills in operation, all on the coast and in association with sawmill complexes. As happened in sawmilling, a rapid expansion of the industry took place in the interior. Output there, however, is necessarily based on smaller-diameter Douglas fir logs and the product grade is generally lower than that from the coast. In consequence, plywood from interior mills does not generally enter export markets, which are concentrated in the United Kingdom and continental Europe. By 1969 there were 22 veneer and plywood plants, half of them in the interior, the capacity concentration being on the southwest coast, especially in the Vancouver area. The 1970 output totalled 1¾ billion square feet (⅜ inch basis) compared with slightly over 1 billion square feet in 1960.

As a reflection of the competitive advantages of construction-grade plywood, the industry has expanded rapidly and now takes nearly one-quarter of the Douglas fir cut, at the same time providing peeler-core and trimming residue for pulp-mills. Latterly, and partly as a result of refined technology, use of other species, notably spruce, has gained momentum and it is not unreasonable to expect new plywood mills to be built in association with integrated interior operations.

PRODUCT TRENDS AND SPATIAL PATTERNS

New capital investment by the combined forest industries has been a major force in the growth of the provincial economy for more than a decade. In 1970 it amounted to nearly $375 million, roughly half of it associated with pulp and paper milling (*Summary of Economic Activity*, 1970). Analyses of market demand suggest that sustained growth of the forest industries can be expected in British Columbia (see, for example, *Pulp and Paper* ... , LXXII, 2 [Feb.], 1971). For export markets, western Canadian producers are in a strong competitive position and are expected to remain so over the next decade. Product quality and cost advantages related to scale of production and to integration are regarded as the chief propellants to maintaining this position.[18] The fact that western seaboard ports are ice-free the year round has also been advantageous. The long-term prospects for kraft pulp and paper appear to be especially promising, based in part upon anticipated Japanese requirements and upon expansion of the large United States market.

Persistence of the Traditional Core
As noted earlier, the cut from provincial forests can be doubled without depleting the resource, assuming present levels of management. Under more intensive management and advanced silviculture, the total annual yield might be increased threefold on a sustained-yield basis. Whether or not the corresponding product output would reflect the traditional emphasis on sawn lumber is questionable. There is some probability that with shorter forest rotation periods (a combination of economic and technical rotations) and changing market requirements, more advanced processing and greater product diversification will ensue. In the future, British Columbia's forests are more likely to be looked upon as generators of cellulose than simply as sources of timber and wood chips. Whatever the product emphasis, it seems probable that the spatial patterns of the forest industry will continue to exhibit strong regional differentiation. Because the wood and wood processing industry is oriented basically towards raw material, those areas possessing greatest forest growth potential are likely to hold the key to the future pattern. In his respect the traditional centre – Vancouver Island and the southwestern mainland – must be regarded as the most important region. Dramatic expansion has occurred and is occur-

18   The Economics and Statistics Branch has reported that wood costs per ton of pulp produced were substantially lower in British Columbia than in its prime competitive areas – eastern Canada, southern United States, Scandinavia, and Finland – (*The Pulp and Paper Industry of British Columbia*, 1970).

ing in the central and northern interior, but that expansion is based mainly upon the allocation of previously untapped forests. On the southwest coast, the industry has passed that stage and now looks to more intensive production, taking advantage of superior biomass potential and desirable species mix, to provide for the needs of future development.

6 The Georgia Strait Urban Region

WALTER G. HARDWICK

Origins and Urban Character of the Region
Most of the urban population of British Columbia is clustered around Georgia Strait in the southwestern corner of the province. Victoria, founded in 1843, Nanaimo (1852), New Westminster (1858), and Vancouver (1886) are the historic cores and present nuclei around which the region is organized. Each city has its unique character and distinctive origin, but continued growth in population, associated with economic expansion and improved accessibility within the region, is contributing to increased functional interdependence.

To most residents, each city functions as an independent entity, even though the cities of the region may be viewed systematically as an emerging megalopolis. Individuals maintain notions of where they live that do not reflect the reality uncovered by geographic analysis. Few local residents would identify their particular city as part of the Georgia Strait region. An appreciation of the region therefore has to proceed at two scales: for each city an evolving geography can be described and, simultaneously, in keeping with a trend from independence to interdependence, an urban regional geography can also be discerned.

The Georgia Strait urban region in 1972 can be described as a dispersed city, a galaxy of subcommunities, of which the inner city of Vancouver is clearly the focus. The fact that this region straddles a large body of water, the Strait of Georgia, differentiates it from many other metropolitan areas. The southwestern mainland of British Columbia and the southeastern shore of Vancouver Island are part of one of the world's most beautiful regions. To the northeast, on the doorstep of Vancouver, the Coast Mountains rise four to six thousand feet from the protected waters, creating a spectacular barrier from the rest of Canada. To the west the lower mountains of Vancouver Island shield the region from the Pacific Ocean and its associated weather. To the south the boundary with the United States of America runs through the lower Fraser River valley and then threads through the myriad of islands that lie in Georgia Strait. Vancou-

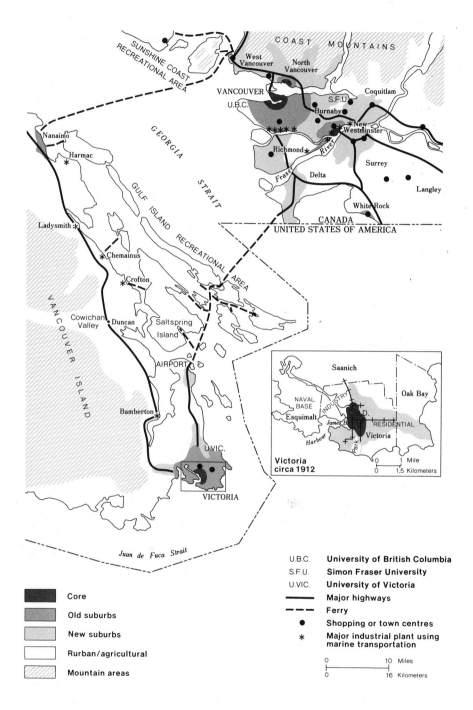

6.1
Georgia Strait Urban Region, 1972

ver and New Westminster with their suburbs have merged into a metropolis of a million people; Victoria with its suburbs on the Saanich peninsula, and Nanaimo 60 miles to the north, lie on the southeast coast of Vancouver Island.

Vancouver might have emerged as a classic primate centre, relegating the Vancouver Island cities to obscurity, except for the fact that Victoria is the seat of the provincial government and Georgia Strait offered unusual opportunities for linking, low-cost marine transportation. The separation of management of the private sector in Vancouver and the public sector of the provincial government in Victoria created complementary activities which made interaction inevitable. Further, the two cities now share an ex-urban hinterland in the islands of Georgia Strait. The dispersal of corporately linked industrial plants around the Strait, rather than centralized in Vancouver, is a more impressive, and a more unusual reason, for community interaction.

From the late nineteenth century until World War ii, the relationship between the communities was one of rivalry as the founding generations used their cities as meccas for individual opportunity. As in many places across the continent, the frontier optimism slowly faded as the realities of a limited resource base and the particular relative location of each community came into sharper perspective. Slowly the cities became drawn together.

Victoria became the colonial capital following the evacuation of the Columbia River Territory south of the 49th parallel by the Hudson's Bay Company in 1843. Its strategic location on the southern tip of Vancouver Island established British claims to all of the island, and in addition provided an excellent sheltered port on the Strait of Juan de Fuca. As trade expanded on the Pacific, Victoria became a regular port of call for sailing ships rounding Cape Horn from England or inbound from Asia. Later, with the discovery of gold on the British Columbia mainland and expansion of travel from California, it functioned as an entrepôt for interior British Columbia, as San Francisco did a decade earlier for the Sacramento and San Joaquin Valleys of California (see Chapter 2).

New Westminster, occupying the high bank where the Fraser River divides into its delta distributaries, acted as the first administrative centre on the mainland. The colonial capital of British Columbia for a brief period, 1858–68, the city soon attracted sawmills and provided a market for the farms of the Fraser Valley. Nanaimo, in contrast, was a coal-mining town, and the Nanaimo area mines in the nineteenth century were major suppliers of coal to many Pacific ports, including San Francisco.

Vancouver's incorporation awaited the arrival of the transcontinental railway to the coast in 1886. Burrard Inlet had been the site of sawmill operations a generation before the Canadian Pacific Railway was completed, and was a very small settlement. With the opening of the railway and the shift in orientation of the region from Britain and western America to Canada, changes in the role of the cities were inevitable.

Despite the rising challenge of Vancouver interests, Victoria throughout the nineteenth century maintained its status as the centre of government, commerce, and trade. However, by the time of World War I, the challenge of Vancouver people in commerce, finance, and industry was largely successful and Victoria had been eclipsed. Victoria maintained the executive and legislative branches of government, but over the years other provincial services have been increasingly located in downtown Vancouver.

The region's cities, first Victoria and then Vancouver, provided the transportation articulation function that must be expected where international seaborne traffic and landward transportation corridors come together. Today, Georgia Strait functions as an integrated port for Canada's west coast (Kerfoot 1966).

Although Nanaimo's coal brought the region into international prominence, it was forestry that provided the region with a continuing export commodity. Lumber was shipped abroad as soon as Europeans occupied the territory. As the forest industry became thoroughly integrated (see Chapter 5), it contributed not only to a sound economic base, but also to the functional interconnection of integrated plants fully utilizing logs for a variety of wood products such as lumber, plywood, pulp, paper, and shingles (Hardwick 1963).

The extractive industries, the port, the railroad, and the construction industry offered job opportunities to thousands of immigrants, many lacking skills or training, but each eager to work and establish himself and his family in a new country and where possible on his own plot of land. It was a frontier, one that in less than a century has become urbanized.

In the process, stress and conflict on resource and urban environment issues have taken place. The first immigrants came to make fortunes by exploiting the environment, an objective passed on to their children. Later-generation residents and many recent immigrants have recognized the quality of the coastal environment and have begun to work to preserve and enhance it. To one group the quality environment assures the good life, to the other raw materials assure economic growth and employment. These contrasting views are important in shaping the future of the region as a whole as it becomes mega-urbanized and subject to higher population densities.

The Georgia Strait region has a regional identity easily defined in physical environmental terms. Only in the last two decades has its extent been defined in human geographic terms. Although the native Indians occupied land near many river mouths, harvesting the salmon, roots, and berries for 5000 years, their imprint on the landscape was imperceptible (see Chapter 2). The fur traders, loggers, miners, and seamen, as well as the European frontiersmen, barely penetrated the edge of the region's resources. Even the cities of the early twentieth century, though urban in their cores, merged on their margins into the great northwest forest.

With the rapid expansion of population and economic activity in the years since World War II, all this has changed. The cities have spread across tens of square miles of the region. The smog that accumulates with extended high-pressure ridges over the region not only domes over the cities, but extends across the water itself. The valleys and mountain slopes, once covered with virgin forest, are criss-crossed with logging roads which are scars of recent or past logging. Logs have in turn been trucked and towed to the sawmills and pulp-mills in the industrial cores of the region. Bays and channels, once shared by the heron and gull, are lined with cottages or ribbon towns, while a large flotilla of small pleasure craft dots the water surface.

In the past twenty years, then, the visual presence of man is unmistakable. This has coincided with the growth of people, goods, and ideas moving through a web of communications less easily seen on the landscape. Moreover, this has been a product of institutional change as the frontiersman gave way to the capitalist entrepreneur, and he, in turn, to the corporation. The Georgia Strait *urban* region has been emerging in the 1950s and 1960s. Its skeletal framework is in evidence and if the processes of population expansion, institutional centralization, and corporate integration continue, its urban character will be further fleshed out.

Vancouver

During the first decade after incorporation the city occupied only the land which comprises the present downtown peninsula. Within this small area, land uses became differentiated in a fashion that reflected the mix of activities of the founding peoples and provided a preview of the pattern of city development that was to continue up to World War II. Although the city spread across the False Creek industrial waterway in search of land to accommodate the 100,000 persons who arrived in the first decade of this century, the segregation of work and residence, and segregation among social classes persisted. In internal pattern, the city took on a sectoral form around a high-density core. Radiating outward along streetcar lines,

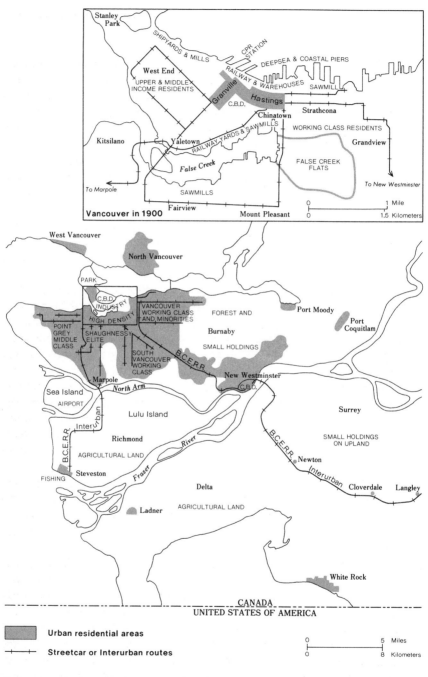

Vancouver in 1900

Stanley Park

SHIPYARDS & MILLS

CPR STATION

DEEPSEA & COASTAL PIERS

West End

UPPER & MIDDLE INCOME RESIDENTS

RAILWAY & WAREHOUSES

SAWMILL

Granville

Hastings

C.B.D.

Chinatown

Strathcona

Kitsilano

Yaletown

RAILWAY YARDS & SAWMILLS

MILLS

WORKING CLASS RESIDENTS

Grandview

False Creek

FALSE CREEK FLATS

To Marpole

SAWMILLS

To New Westminster

Fairview

Mount Pleasant

0   1 Mile

0   1.5 Kilometers

West Vancouver

North Vancouver

PARK

C.B.D.

INDUSTRY

VANCOUVER WORKING CLASS AND MINORITIES

FOREST AND

Port Moody

Port Coquitlam

HIGH DENSITY

POINT GREY MIDDLE CLASS

SHAUGHNESSY ELITE

Burnaby

SMALL HOLDINGS

B.C.E.R.R.

SOUTH VANCOUVER WORKING CLASS

Marpole

New Westminster

C.B.D.

Sea Island

North Arm

AIRPORT

Lulu Island

Surrey

Interurban

B.C.E.R.R.

SMALL HOLDINGS ON UPLAND

Richmond

River

AGRICULTURAL LAND

Fraser

B.C.E.R.R.

Newton

Interurban

Cloverdale

Langley

Steveston

FISHING

Delta

Ladner

AGRICULTURAL LAND

White Rock

CANADA

UNITED STATES OF AMERICA

Urban residential areas

Streetcar or Interurban routes

0   5 Miles

0   8 Kilometers

6.2
Lower Mainland, including Vancouver, the Radial City, 1920–45

neighbourhoods of single-family detached houses accommodated variously the elite, professional, and trades and working classes. Near the core a transition zone of industry (the outskirts of the 1890 city) provided a secondary employment focus. This pattern, clearly defined by 1920, persisted until the 1950s, during which time the population expanded from 22,000 in 1900 to 400,000 people.

The land beyond, some six miles from the core, was occupied by farms, rural homesteads, and small sawmills. On the Fraser delta lush dairy and berry farms prospered; to the east on the forest-covered glacial deposition upon which much of Vancouver and Burnaby sits, farms were little more than clearings in the woods. Twelve to fifteen miles beyond, Port Moody and New Westminster were service towns largely independent of Vancouver. The urban use of this peripheral land awaited World War II (Hardwick 1971).

The contrasting views of the city held by professional and management groups on the one hand and the immigrant working class on the other were evident from the day the city was founded. Not only did the various groups separate residentially, their distinctive roles were in evidence in the commercial land uses as well. Vancouver was founded as a great city – it was no small town that grew. Notwithstanding its sawmill and railway origins, it was to be the 'Terminal City by the Sunset Sea' – a mercantile city where the transcontinental railroad met the trans-Pacific steamer. The visions of the logger and the visions of the city builder were different. This became manifest in a binodal downtown and in the very organization of the residential suburbs. It is still evident in political forums on environmental questions.

Downtown, in the 1890s, the 'Gastown area' along the waterfront was the most important part of town (Morley 1961). The stores, offices, and hostelries rapidly expanded in number, creating a moving construction frontier from Water Street to Cordova and Hastings Streets before expanding west. On the waterfront were the coastal steamer piers and ferry wharves, and the electric interurban railway from the Fraser Valley terminated on Hastings Street. The locally owned department store was also on Hastings Street, as were the burlesque, cafes, and hotels for working men in from the camps and mines and off the ships and trains. These streets became the commercial core for the people from the east side of the city. The other core was Granville Street, on higher ground to the west, the site of the CPR hotel and quality shops. The Granville core catered to the elite groups from the West End and to travellers from around the world. Prestige offices, occupied by professional people servicing the well-to-do members of the community, the Court House, and major churches filled out this western core. Later, motion picture theatres and other hotels were added. The binodal core was a reality.

The two nodes were linked by Hastings Street, a corridor which attracted financial and business services. The Dominion Bank Building was constructed at Hastings and Cambie Streets in the first decade of the 1900s, and other financial houses followed suit, establishing Hastings as the city's financial row. This emphasis was maintained throughout the following decades with a westward spread being evident in the 1960s.

To the south, on the border of the incipient community in the 1890s, sawmills and other industrial plants edged False Creek. To the east, along the harbour, warehouses and mills took advantage of water and rail access. These sections remained the dominant industrial areas until the pattern changed dramatically in the 1960s.

Residentially the growing city became segregated as elite and professional and business middle class settled the West End toward Stanley Park. Formal, tree-lined streets were laid out, lined by two- and three-storey frame homes with verandas and elegant front gardens. By the 1920s this type of housing expanded to the southwest into Shaughnessy and Point Grey. In the early years entrepreneurial groups engaged in construction and local resource exploitation settled on the east sides of Vancouver, in Strathcona, Grandview, and Mount Pleasant. To the south near the False Creek mills, working men's neighbourhoods were founded by CPR land agents who sold 25-foot lots at low prices so as to attract millworkers and railworkers. Later, around 1910, these people and those who joined them expanded into Mount Pleasant and then into South Vancouver, creating their own municipality. Some were prosperous and built homes as large as any in the West End. These people in east and south Vancouver had different attitudes toward their environment than those in the west. The recentness of the city, and the availability of streetcar transportation within a couple of years founding of the city, allowed everyone who wanted a lot and a house to have one. The building of detached homes was the rule; the building of tenements or shops with residences above was the exception.

Close to downtown were the Oriental ghettos, particularly Chinese and Japanese. Excluded from many trades and professions, these people developed highly integrated and relatively self-sufficient communities. One other minority played a distinctive role in the development of Vancouver – the East Indian colony that lived adjacent to the sawmills south of False Creek. Tolerance of minorities was not a virtue of the Anglo-Saxon community and racial friction was commonplace. Large immigrant groups from Europe, common in Eastern Canada and on the Prairies, were not present in large numbers in the early years. However, Italian and German neighbourhoods became visible after World War II.

By the late 1920s Vancouver city had developed the internal structure and character which still persists. The high-density core with its two shopping streets, the financial district, and adjacent warehouse areas provided most of the jobs. Nearby the waterfront docks, railyards, and sawmills added to the variety of opportunity. Further out some high-density and converted residences occupied the buffer between the inner city and the residential suburbs. This pattern, served by the streetcars, became legislated by the zoning by-laws and the amalgamation of Vancouver with its adjacent suburbs in 1929.

Through the years of deprivation – the depression years of the 1930s and wartime – little new construction took place in the city. The landscape of the 1920s became a familiar scene to local residents. To many the city had been completed in rough. The future was to be spent improving it.

Urban Growth since 1950
Population growth was renewed during World War II and continued after the war. Thousands of new residents had to be accommodated in dwellings and jobs. Fortunately the economic expansion provided jobs and dwellings, but in doing so, several major changes took place in city patterns.

Expanding populations were not forced to leap frog existing neighbourhoods to the south and east, but instead changed the direction of settlement to the North Shore of Burrard Inlet. This was made possible by a new bridge which was constructed across Burrard Inlet in the late 1930s, and which made the North Shore an instant suburb.

The expansion of industrial production that took place after World War II was not centred in the earlier industrial areas of False Creek and Burrard Inlet. Peripheral sites were sought for sawmills, oil refineries, paper plants, and even large warehousing establishments. Plants spread along the Fraser River east of New Westminster, which shared in the growth. Later, regional shopping centres along major arterial highways brought shopping convenience and other employment opportunities to the peripheral municipalities. Universities, airports, and provincial hospitals were among the growing public institutions outside the old radial city. Dairy farms and stump farms alike, to the south and east, fell to the subdivider as the automobile-oriented suburbs became established. In the process, the urban system changed scale from the 2-mile radius of 1900 to a 6-mile radius in 1920, to a 10-mile radius in 1950, and to a 20-mile radius in 1960 – and towards the Georgia Strait region in the 1970s.

In the process of dispersion, adjustments have taken place in the function of the core. Some old inner-city neighbourhoods were privately redeveloped for high-rise apartment living. Industrial areas such as False Creek began to be abandoned by industry. Shopping, under competition from regional shopping centres, became an ancillary service to the work force of the major propellent of downtown: management of resources, economy, transportation, and other private and public services. A shift in employment away from the primary and secondary sectors to tertiary and quaternary contributed to the population dispersion, and the changing relationships between the core and suburbs. Structural changes in employment are reflected in the social class orientation of the population and, as noted before, in their values vis-à-vis the city and its environment. The affluence and leisure of the population are increasing the demand for recreational facilities and pushing that frontier outward into the exclusive territories of formerly independent communities. Integration of the whole region is in part accommodating the metropolitan role of Vancouver and its inhabitants.

New Westminster
This city's importance is underrated by the census figure of 42,000 people. It is the centre of some 250,000 people living south and east on both banks of the Fraser River. Its growth was slow in the last century, but the fleeting period of the Gold Rush gave it its start. The sawmills, fish canneries, and farmers provided its sustained growth. Later, as navigation on the Fraser improved, its port and railway functions expanded. New Westminster, the Royal City, was fully independent of Vancouver in the early part of the century. Its main streets, paralleling the Fraser River, were well developed with shops and offices and bustling with pedestrians. The interurban railway depot, continuing the practice initiated by the river steamers' dock, acted as the focus for a farm trade area in the eastern Fraser Valley. The farmers' market and similar institutions marked New Westminster as a typical Canadian service town. The prominent homes on the hill overlooking the river showed the presence of local wealth and a certain social stability. The sawmills to the east and west offered a continuing source of jobs for immigrants, including the French Canadians who settled in Maillardville. The government offices serving the Fraser Valley gave it its administrative role.

New Westminster has undergone some of the same building changes as seen in downtown Vancouver. In particular several old neighbourhoods adjacent to downtown have become high-rise apartment districts. Old industrial areas near downtown have become obsolete as expanding businesses search out new and larger sites, including an uptown retail district within the north-central part of the city.

After World War II, New Westminster's immediate hinterland was surrounded by an expanding Vancouver and its independence was challenged. Although it maintains a steady growth and continues to serve as an eastern core to the metropolitan region, it has been further integrated into the Georgia Strait urban system. This is manifest in the commuter traffic which bypasses the city and the radio station that leads all others in listeners in the Greater Vancouver region. Like other cities captured in a metropolis, traditions in New Westminster are maintained – and its distinctive identity in culture, sports, and community action remains.

Nanaimo

Nanaimo is one of several communities around Georgia Strait that once were independent, based upon the export of raw materials – timber or minerals. Prior to World War II these towns were connected to the big cities by coastal steamers; they were masters of their own destinies, as long as their resources were not exhausted.

Nanaimo was a typical mining town early in this century. Rows of single-storey frame homes lined the streets overlooking the bay; many were company-owned. Nearby a sawmill cut timber for use in the mines. A small commercial core spread along a winding street between the steamer dock and the Esquimalt and Nanaimo Railway station. Nanaimo looked like, and functioned like, any other resource town of the Cordillera. Its changing role really came after World War II when the mines closed (Robinson 1965).

The construction of a pulp-mill, and the expansion of logging operations to the west into the Nanaimo Lakes, created new industry integrated into the MacMillan and Bloedel Company operations. Some of the logs from the area went to the Harmac pulp-mill south of Nanaimo, but most did not. They were sent to the Fraser River mills for conversion into lumber, plywood, shingles, or other products. In return pulpwood chips, a by-product of the sawmills, were barged back to Nanaimo to become a raw material for the pulp and paper operations. Such corporate integration contributes to the integration of the Georgia Strait region (Robinson and Hardwick 1968).

Transportation links to other centres changed in the post-war years. The improvements of the road system on Vancouver Island prompted a shift from coastal steamers to truck deliveries. Nanaimo, the nearest port to Vancouver, was a natural distribution centre. Rather than shipping goods from Vancouver docks to various outports along Georgia Strait, warehousing was moved to Nanaimo, along with oil distributors, and similar facilities. In addition, rail, truck, and automobile service to the central and northern island was transferred to the so-called 'Hub City.' Ferries with capacities of up to 200 automobiles operate hourly between Vancouver and Nanaimo. This is not only a one-way movement, however. Nanaimo shoppers can day-trip to Vancouver or attend major sports or cultural activities.

Nanaimo was always a working man's town. This is changing with the opening of Malaspina Regional College and the expansion of local management, professions, and trade services. Although separated by water from Vancouver, it functions like New Westminster or other Fraser Valley towns as part of the urban region.

Victoria

Victoria and its adjoining municipalities have a heritage of Victorian urbanity that was not shared by the other cities in the region. In the last century it was a colonial capital linked to the mother country and to other colonial centres of the Pacific. Its important citizens were not so much entrepreneurs of the American frontier as civil servants and professional people schooled in Britain and Scotland. Their attitudes about cities and landscape contributed to the English heritage that has continued to the present day.

The city had its origins around James Bay and the inner harbour, with the government buildings to the south and the commercial and industrial facilities to the north. Douglas and Government Streets, now the major shopping streets, acted as the main axis of the incipient community with wharves, foundries, and ship-builders lining the harbour. To the north were the farms of the Saanich peninsula and to the west the Royal Navy Shipyards at Esquimalt (see Figure 6.1).

As in the case of Vancouver, the area occupied by Victoria in the early years was small. Nevertheless the separation of land uses by function became clear; and the city of the nineteenth century became the commercial core of this mid-century. The James Bay area and land adjoining Beacon Hill Park, the major city park south of the core, have become an apartment district, similar to the West End of Vancouver. Industrial land uses have remained along the inner harbour waterfront. The old warehouses and transportation centre along the inner harbour is now characterized as a 'zone of discard,' reflecting the change of function and change in relative location of the city. In the days when Victoria was the commercial and transportation hub of the region, most goods were shipped in and out by sea. However, with Vancouver taking over many of these functions, the harbour no longer had this transshipment function and became relegated to tugboat docks, small shipyards and industrial plants, including sawmills. As is the case with Vancouver's False Creek, Victoria's harbour fringe is rapidly being redeveloped for commercial and residential uses in the 1970s.

Some docks in the inner harbour maintained their importance as passenger ship docks for many years, serving steamers from Vancouver and Seattle and at a later time ferries from the Olympic peninsula. Until 1960 the Canadian Pacific steamers to Victoria were, in effect, extensions of the transcontinental railways and their schedules met the trains in Vancouver. The ships were modelled after British Channel steamers and made the runs to the mainland cities in about five hours. However, they became obsolete when the government initiated an automobile-oriented ferry system across the Strait of Georgia, cutting ship time to one hour and forty minutes (essentially extending the highway system). These hourly ferries brought Victoria into Vancouver's orbit, and truck terminals along the highways north of Victoria replaced the old dock-side warehouses. Large semi-trailers now leave Vancouver warehouses with supplies for supermarkets and deliver them in Victoria the same morning. In this way the relationship of Victoria to Vancouver parallels that of the Fraser Valley towns which are served from Vancouver warehouses.

Victoria has been undergoing private urban renewal in the core, partly by new construction and partly by reconstruction of the old, such as Bastion Square near the City Hall. Public open space and street furniture are intensively manicured, in part to maintain the tourist image of England planted in offshore America. In the downtown, government buildings, fine hotels, historic churches, and stores are grouped within walking distance of one another, a fact found very attractive by visitors.

Residential areas, originally close in, spread east and north in the 1920s to occupy not only Victoria but also the adjoining municipalities of Oak Bay, Esquimalt, and Saanich. To the east in Oak Bay, elegant gardens and an atmosphere of quality living is in evidence, in part reflecting a view of an urban landscape held in the elite areas of Vancouver. Fine homes built amid oaks and arbutus trees upon the promontories overlooking the sea and the Olympic Mountains to the south add a dimension reflecting the British colonial past. In their midst a golf course was built, modelled after the St Andrew's course in Scotland. Between Oak Bay and downtown Victoria, many neighbourhoods have an appearance similar to working-class neighbourhoods in east-side Vancouver.

To the north on Saanich peninsula small subdivisions of modern bungalows provide the suburban sprawl known to most automobile-oriented North American cities. Ranch-style houses are interspersed among old farms and woodlots. The spread of the urban population outward is the subject of study by the Capital Regional District planners. As expected, regional shopping centres have been built to serve the new suburbs and, increasingly, new work-places are springing up on the periphery, the University of Victoria being an example.

Victoria has become a retirement centre for eastern Canadians. Hundreds of people have moved there and to southeastern Vancouver Island to enjoy the moderate climate and the small-city atmosphere. This adds to the distinctiveness of Victoria as a city within the Georgia Strait urban region.

Regional Government
Interdependence of communities in the lower mainland of British Columbia and around Georgia Strait is a new reality (see Chapter 4). Many measures of spatial interaction including ship movements and telephone calls testify to this. However, public institutions are slow to react, and this in turn has consequences for the future of the region. The political realities are that residents see themselves as members of local towns and cities and do not visualize the wider interdependence. Politically, therefore, it is difficult to move to regional government. The provincial government has established regional districts which collectively involve all the communities. However, only in Greater Vancouver and Greater Victoria are these district bodies well staffed and adopting important policy-oriented roles. There is, however, no co-ordination of plans between the two regional districts. In contrast, many firms engaged in wholesale distribution, forest products manufacturing, communications, and shipping are organized on a total regional basis.

It seems clear that as the essential unity of the region comes to be recognized politically as well as economically, considerable adjustment on the part of local political interests will be necessary. Possibly the initial foci of adjustment might well turn out to be precisely those metropolitan characteristics noted above in the discussion of Vancouver, those flowing from the high mobility and affluence of the nodal populations – a concern for the general as opposed to the particular environment of daily life. Some evidence for this hypothesis can be seen in a recent unpublished report from the University of British Columbia on the Recreational Hinterland of the Georgia Strait Region, a study which contributed to the provincial government's decision to control land uses in the Gulf Islands. Additional support is offered by recent provincial and federal concern to protect the region from polluting agencies: there is, for example, a suggestion that the entire Strait be named a national marine park. If this suggestion, or any one similar to it in scope and scale, were to find support, and eventual fruition, it could not fail to have a far-reaching effect on the body politic. It could, indeed, be the catalyst to generate sufficient popular interest to carry over into more detailed, integrated political reforms designed to recognize the unity of the Georgia Strait urban region.

The emerging megalopolis of the far west in Canada is the Georgia Strait urban region. Increased population growth seems inevitable, given the amenities of the region and the great opportunities for a distinctive life style. The record of the past decade suggests that some migrants come without secure job opportunities, but are optimistic about future expectations. Expansion of job opportunities goes together with population growth, but the lag between the two elements often creates temporary individual hardship and political conflict. It seems that these are penalties some people are willing to accept to enjoy what Premier W.A.C. Bennett calls the 'good life.' It is this new consciousness of the quality of the region that is both a liability and an asset. It is a problem in the sense that so many people are attracted to the region. It is an asset because the people are jealous of the quality of the region and are increasingly willing to pay for the maintenance of this uniqueness and quality.

Bibliography

The provincial government is a major source of information about British Columbia. Most of the government departments issue annual and also some specific reports dealing with topics for which they have administrative responsibility. Thus, a wide range of technical and popular reports on forests and forestry; geology, mines, and mining; fish and fisheries; lands and agriculture; rivers and power, etc. may be obtained upon request to the appropriate government department in Victoria. In some cases, such as fisheries or water flows, the federal government is a good source of information. Some specific examples of provincial booklets are the Land Series bulletins for each of ten regions of British Columbia prepared by the former Geographic Division, Department of Lands, Forests and Water Resources, and the Economic Survey reports of several towns or regions prepared by the Economics and Statistics Branch, Department of Industrial Development, Trade and Commerce. A wide range of maps, map indexes, and air photos may be purchased from the Map Production Division, B.C. Department of Lands in Victoria.

The British Columbia Natural Resources Conference has published an excellent series of annual proceedings (vol. 1, 1948, to vol. 18, 1969), which deal with specific themes concerning problems and development trends in each of the major resource fields. The same organization published the *British Columbia Atlas of Resources* in 1956, but this is now out of print.

At the subprovincial level British Columbia is now divided into regional districts, many of which publish reports from their planning boards. Examples are the Capital District Planning reports, which describe urban growth and problems near Victoria, and the several useful reports on the Lower Fraser River Valley prepared by the former Lower Mainland Regional Planning Board (now Greater Vancouver Regional District). Among the publications of several corporations and public institutions some of the most useful are issued by the B.C. Hydro and Power Authority in Vancouver.

The major sources of geographic research and publication are the geography departments of the three provincial universities: University of British Columbia (Vancouver), Simon Fraser University (Burnaby), University of Victoria (Victoria). Many of the unpublished graduate theses from U.B.C. were used as sources for material in chapters in this book and not recorded in the chapter references. Each geography department will furnish lists of unpublished theses upon request.

The Western (formerly B.C.) Division of the Canadian Association of Geographers publishes its annual proceedings of papers and other articles, beginning with number 1 in 1960. Most of these articles deal with geographical aspects of British Columbia. The centre of publication for the Western Division of the Association has changed from time to time, but the current executive can be reached through any of the three university geography departments. Associated with, but separate from, the Western Division of the Association is the B.C. Geographical Series published by Tantalus Press, Box 4248, Vancouver 9, which now comprises 16 booklets by B.C. geographers, beginning with number 1 published in 1964. The reference lists for the chapters in the present volume follow.

Chapter 2

Akrigg, Helen B., 1964   History and Economic Development of the Shuswap Area (unpublished MA Thesis, UBC)

Borden, Charles E., 1968   Prehistory of the Lower Mainland, Chap. 1 in A.H. Siemens (ed.), *The Lower Fraser Valley: Evolution of a Cultural Landscape* (Vancouver: Tantalus): 9–26

Duff, W., 1965   *The Indian History of B.C.*, Anthropology in B.C. Memoir No. 5 (Victoria: Queen's Printer)

Ormsby, M.A., 1945   Agricultural Development in British Columbia, *Agricultural History*, 19 (Jan.): 11–20

— 1958   *British Columbia: A History* (Toronto: Macmillan)

Richter, J.J., 1964   The Developing Pattern of B.C. Agriculture, *Transactions of 15th B.C. Natural Resources Conference* (Victoria: Queen's Printer): 151–64

Siemens, Alfred H. (ed.), 1968   *The Lower Fraser Valley: Evolution of a Cultural Landscape* (Vancouver: Tantalus Press)

Vanderhill, Burke G., 1963   Trends in the Peace River Country, *Can. Geog.*, 7: 33–41

Weir, Thomas R., 1964   *Ranching in the Southern Interior Plateau of B.C.* Memoir 4, Geographical Branch (Ottawa)

Chapter 3

Campbell, P.I., Reid, I.A., and Shastal, J., 1969a   *Glacier Survey in Alberta*, Water Survey of Canada, Inland Waters Branch, Report 4

— 1969b   *Glacier Surveys in British Columbia*, Water Survey of Canada, Inland Waters Branch, Report 5

Canada Land Inventory, 1966   *Agroclimatological Atlas of British Columbia*

Chapman, J.D., 1952   The Climate of British Columbia, *Transactions of 5th B.C. Natural Resources Conference*: 8–54

Holland, S.S., 1964   *Landforms of British Columbia*, B.C. Dept. of Mines and Petroleum Resources, Bull. 48

Jeffrey, W.W., 1968   Watershed Management Problems in British Columbia: A First Appraisal, *Water Resources Bull.*, 4: 58–70

Mathews, W.H., 1947   Tuyas, Flat Topped Volcanoes in Northern British Columbia, *Amer. J. Science*, 245: 560–70

— 1955   *Ground Water Possibilities of the Peace River Block*, B.C. Dept. of Mines, Groundwater Paper 3

— 1956   Physical Limnology and Sedimentation in a Glacial Lake, *Bull. Geol. Soc. Amer.*, 67: 537–52

— 1963   *Quaternary Stratigraphy and Geomorphology of the Fort St. John Area*, B.C. Dept. of Mines and Petroleum Resources

Mathews, W.H., and Shepard, F.P., 1962   Sedimentation of Fraser River Delta, *Ann. Assoc. Pet. Geol.*, 46: 1416–43

Ostrem, G., 1966a   Mass Balance Studies on Glaciers in Western Canada, *Geog. Bull.*, 8: 81–107

— 1966b   The Height of the Glaciation Limit in Southern British Columbia and Alaska, *Geog. Ann.*, 48A: 126–38

Quick, M.C., 1965   River Flows, Forecasts and Probabilities, *J. Hydraulics Division, Amer. Soc. Civ. Engrs.*, 91, HY3: 1–18

Ryder, J.M., 1971   The Stratigraphy and Morphology of Paraglacial Alluvial Fans in South Central British Columbia, *Can. J. Earth Sciences*, 8: 279–98

Sediment Survey of Canada, 1955–67   *Sediment Data for Canadian Rivers* (Ottawa: Inland Waters Branch)

Slaymaker, H.O., 1972   Recent Fluctuations in the Mean Discharge of the Fraser River, *in* R. Leigh (ed.), *Contemporary Geography: Research Trends* (Vancouver: Tantalus): 3–13

Slaymaker, H.O., and Jeffrey, W.W., 1969   Physiography-Land Use Interactions in Watershed Management, *in* A.H. Laycock et al. (eds.), *Symposium on Water Balance in North America*: 170–81

Stanley, A.D., 1970   Combined Balance Studies at Selected Glacier Basins in Canada, *Proc. Workshop Seminar on Glaciers, Canadian National Committee*, IHD: 5–9

Thomas, J.F.J., 1953–4   Industrial Water Resources of Canada, *Water Survey Reports* 1, 4, 5, 6

Water Survey of Canada, 1913–67   *Surface Water Data* (Ottawa: Inland Waters Branch)

Chapter 4

Barr, B., 1972   Has the Prairie Region Solved Its Economic Problems?, *in* R. Leigh (ed.), *Contemporary Geography: Research Trends* (Vancouver: Tantalus): 111–21

Economic Council of Canada, 1965   *Second Annual Review* (Ottawa: Queen's Printer)

Employers Council of B.C., 1969   *Limitations and Attractions of B.C. for Industry* (Vancouver)

Government of the Province of B.C., 1960–9   *Industrial Expansion in B.C.* (Victoria: Department of Industrial Development, Trade and Commerce)

Ingram, J., 1958   Industrial Development in B.C., *Canadian Mining and Metallurgical Bull.* (Sept.): 1–5

Lithwick, N., 1968 Regional Contagion, *in* N. Lithwick and G. Paquet (eds.), *Urban Studies: A Canadian Perspective* (Toronto: Methuen)

Lycan, R., and Forrester, E., 1970 Spatial Structure on Vancouver Island, *in* H. Foster (ed.), *Geographica* (Victoria: University of Victoria)

McGovern, P.D., 1961 Industrial Development in the Vancouver Area, *Econ. Geog.* (July): 189–206

Robinson, J.L., and Hardwick, W., 1968 The Canadian Cordillera, Chap. 13 *in* J. Warkentin (ed.), *Canada: A Geographical Interpretation* (Toronto: Methuen)

Shearer, R. (ed.), 1968 *Exploiting Our Economic Potential* (Toronto: Holt, Rinehart and Winston)

Chapter 5

Bowland, J.G., Fitzpatrick, J.M., et al., 1968 *The Use and Production of Construction-Grade Plywood in Canada* (Ottawa: Forest Economics Research Institute, Department of Forestry and Rural Development)

British Columbia Forest Service, Inventory Division, 1969 *Forest Inventory Statistics of British Columbia, 1967* (Victoria: Department of Lands, Forests and Water Resources)

Bureau of Economics and Statistics, 1966 *Selected Forest Industry Statistics of British Columbia, 1965* (Victoria: Department of Industrial Development, Trade and Commerce)

Chapman, J.D., Turner, D., et al., 1956 *British Columbia Atlas of Resources* (Victoria: British Columbia Natural Resources Conference)

Department of Finance, 1970 *Financial and Economic Review* (Victoria: Government of British Columbia)

Dominion Bureau of Statistics, 1969 *Canada Yearbook* (Ottawa: Department of Industry, Trade and Commerce)

— 1970 Publications 35-204 (Sawmills and Planing Mills), 36-204 (Pulp and Paper Mills) and 26-204 (Mineral Industries) (Ottawa: Department of Industry, Trade and Commerce)

Economics and Statistics Branch, 1970 *Summary of Economic Activity in British Columbia, 1970* (Victoria: Department of Industrial Development, Trade and Commerce)

— 1970 *The Pulp and Paper Industry of British Columbia* (Victoria: Department of Industrial Development, Trade and Commerce)

Hagenstein, P.R., 1965 Factors in Locating Pulp Mills, *Pulp and Paper* (San Francisco: Miller-Freeman Publications)

Hall, J.A., 1970 *Wood, Pulp and Paper, and People in the Northwest* (Portland: Pacific Northwest Forest and Range Experiment Station, Forest Service, U.S.D.A.)

Industrial Development Department, 1966 *The Pulp and Paper Industry of British Columbia*, 2nd ed. (Vancouver: British Columbia Hydro and Power Authority)

Lamb, W.K., 1938   Early Lumbering on Vancouver Island, Part ı. 1844–1855, *British Columbia Historical Quarterly*, ıı (Jan.) : 31–53.

Manning, G.H., 1971   Export Demand for Canada's Pulp and Paper 1980 and 2000, *Pulp and Paper Magazine of Canada* LXXII, 2 (Feb.) : 25–9

Newport, C.A., Metcalf, M.E., et al., 1965   *Timber Resource Statistics for the Pacific Northwest as of January 1, 1963* (Portland: Pacific Northwest Forest and Range Experiment Station, Forest Service, U.S.D.A.)

Rich, S.U. (ed.), 1969   *Marketing in the Changing World of the 1970's* (Eugene: Proceedings of the Sixth Annual Forest Industries Marketing Conference, University of Oregon)

Wilson, A.K., and Spencer, J.S., 1967   *Timber Resources and Industries of the Rocky Mountain States* (Ogden: Intermountain Forest and Range Experiment Station, Forest Service, U.S.D.A.)

Chapter 6

Hardwick, Walter G., 1963   *Geography of the Forest Industry of Coastal British Columbia*, Occasional Papers in Geography No. 5 (Vancouver: Tantalus)

— 1971   Vancouver: The Emergence of a Core-Ring Urban Pattern, Chap. 8 *in* L. Gentilcore (ed.), *Geographic Approaches to Canadian Problems* (Scarborough: Prentice-Hall)

Kerfoot, Denis E., 1966   *Port of British Columbia*, B.C. Geographical Series No. 2 (Vancouver: Tantalus)

Morley, Alan, 1961   *Vancouver: From Milltown to Metropolis* (Vancouver: Mitchell Press)

Robinson, J. Lewis, 1965   Nanaimo, B.C., *Can. Geog. J.* (May) : 162–9

Robinson, J. Lewis, and Hardwick, W.G., 1968   The Canadian Cordillera, Chap. 13 *in* John Warkentin (ed.), *Canada. A Geographical Interpretation* (Toronto: Methuen)